also by

PETRA WILLIAMS

Flow Blue China
An Aid to Identification
(1971)

Flow Blue China II
(1973)

Flow Blue China
and
Mulberry Ware

Similarity and Value Guide

NING PO
R. HALL

AURORA
F. MORLEY

CABUL
E. CHALLINOR

WASHINGTON
T. WALKER

MADRAS
DOULTON

EXAMPLES OF
FLOW BLUE
PATTERNS AND
THEIR DUPLICATES
IN MULBERRY.

Petra Williams

Flow Blue China
and
Mulberry Ware

Similarity and Value Guide

*Layout and Photographic Illustrations
for the text by
Marguerite R. Weber*

FOUNTAIN HOUSE EAST
Jeffersontown, Kentucky

Additional Copies of the Book May
Be Obtained from

FOUNTAIN HOUSE EAST
P.O. Box 99298
Jeffersontown, Kentucky 40299

DEDICATED WITH LOVE

TO

the memory of

my Father and Mother

Grover and Mayme Bullock Schatz

FOREWORD

Let us reason together. Victorian Flow Blue China is getting older and older, day by day, year by year. I am sure that this is a source of satisfaction to all of you who have been collecting the handsome ware. You realize that prices have risen and that it costs more to obtain Flow Blue pieces than it did when you started, but you also know that the value of your collection has equally advanced.

In 1860, when early Flow Blue ware was being exported from Staffordshire, England, to the United States, there were little more than 31.4 million people here. Forty years later, at the end of major Flow Blue production, in 1900, the population of the States had more than doubled and was about 76 million. In 1960, according to the United States Census Bureau, the population reached 179 million. The projected figure for 1975 is 223 million.

Although the amount of Flow Blue items has not increased, the number of people who are possible collectors, added to those already collecting Flow Blue, has increased prodigiously, just as the number of persons counted in the census has greatly multiplied.

The study of a given subject, and the subsequent furtherance of knowledge in that field, can often lead to an intensified interest in further research. This is especially true when one studies artifacts and antiques. One feels the lure of the past, daydreams of one's ancestors' romantic and courageous endeavors, longs for the solid religious and moral values that we believe motivated and sustained our forebears. When we hold a piece of Flow Blue and study the hazy dark pattern, and the mark of the maker, it is like holding a token that evokes the past, and the token is treasured.

Fifty years ago, there were not many people interested in our field. In the first place, Flow Blue had not reached antique status, and secondly, those who did have access to the dishes were not particularly impressed with them because their parents had not paid a great deal for them, and they were in common use. Even 15 years ago there were not many people, dealers included, who deemed Flow Blue China a major collecting choice. Sometimes one cannot see the forest for the trees. The humble china that could be found packed away in the attic in boxes was overlooked in the search for historical ware, porcelain and Canton ware. Dealers and collectors enjoy telling me of picking up a piece for 50 cents, or a set for five dollars. They are to be congratulated for their good taste and acumen. They were far ahead of the time when Flow Blue could come into its own and be recognized as antique, interesting, decorative and growing more valuable every day.

Since the publication of my first book, "Flow Blue China, an Aid to Identification", in 1971, the number of collectors has increased yearly, and these probable purchasers are studying the subject, learning to read marks, learning to recognize patterns and how to date the year of manufacture. Their interest is being stimulated by their growing knowledge.

If a lot of people want the same thing, and no more of that thing can be found, its value, as indicated by price, is bound to advance.

Ever so many smart, dedicated and eager collectors are searching for Flow Blue China. Some of them want any piece they can find, others are searching for a particular pattern or part of a special dinner set. It seems to me that every collector I see wants cups and saucers, tea pots and tureens. Of course, these are available, but they are the scarcest items in a limited field and accordingly are priced high.

I said in my first book (1971) that your investment was safe, and that "price is a matter of supply and demand, of course, but your Flow Blue will not depreciate in value, it can only grow older and more valuable." Time has confirmed this statement. The prices quoted in the first book are somewhat the same today for the very late patterns, but the prices of the early patterns have steadily advanced, as the limited supply is subjected to intensified demand.

Mulberry ware is intimately related to the Flow Blue field. Most of it was produced around 1850-1855. It was made by the same potters who were producing Flow Blue and often had the same name and pattern as the blue. Although it is not well known by the collecting public, many astute dealers have been aware of its value for years. The prices have remained stable, and fairly high, but I expect that they will advance in the near future as collectors realize the investment potential and the worthwhile pursuit and acquisition of items in this highly specialized field.

Reasonable people do not go overboard in their expenditures. It is exhilarating, fine fun to locate an antique for which you have been searching, and satisfying to acquire it. I guess we are all (or almost all) alike in being acquisitive, anxious to possess, and jealous of our treasure. We guard it with care and are most reluctant to part with it, but our pain of relinquishment is usually assuaged if we feel that we sold at a fair price. I am no prognosticator and certainly cannot foretell the future, but I do know that if you sell today the Flow Blue items that you purchased in 1971 you will make a profit, and probably a good one. In these days of inflation, one can only hope to keep even with the falling value of the dollar. Certainly Flow Blue has been a good investment to date. Excepting only in times of severe economic depression, there are always collectors and entrepreneurs who continue to buy and invest in antique objects. If you can hold your collection throughout depressed periods, it will always maintain its value and in all probability will continue its upward trend.

Collecting Flow Blue China and Mulberry ware should not be considered a primary investment, but if you enjoy the history and romantic aura of the patterns, and get pleasure from displaying your treasure and do not rob yourself of necessities or take away from emergency funds in order to indulge in what amounts to a luxury, if you can afford the purchase price and understand the value of the item you are buying, there would seem to be no reason to deny the collector's itch and do so with a feeling of satisfaction and security.

To paraphrase Gertrude Stein, an antique is an antique, is an antique, is an antique: It cannot be repeated too often. An antique cannot be made today, it cannot be mass produced, (even if it was one of many made long ago). It cannot be duplicated. Antiques can be copied; they cannot be duplicated. Marks are marks, and if you know your pottery marks you cannot be easily cheated. If you doubt the authenticity of a mark, do reference work before you part with your money on a modern production. Go to the library, do your home work. Read the books listed in the bibliography of my first two books. Learn the subject well, after all if you are going to be a serious collector and not just an impulse buyer, you must protect yourself by schooling yourself to become as expert as you can be. It is not easy to fool a person who is on the alert, and who has become educated in a particular field such as ours. It is not a difficult study, the facts are available. I am not a know-it-all, although some dealers complain that I think I am. There is always something more to learn and I am eager to discover and study any new developments that occur in my particular field of interest. I am glad to share with you the material I have gleaned about Flow Blue and Mulberry ware.

Because no woman is an island unto herself, I certainly did not gain this knowledge sitting alone in Jeffersontown. Many people helped me and my gratitude is hereby expressed to collectors like Ed Savage, who found "Turin", Ruth Kautz, Mary Sable, Trude Whitehall and Shirley Frantzel, who located "Anglesea" and "Bonita", and to the many others who sent corrections, discovered additional patterns and sent information.

This book was not easy to compile insofar as the value lists were concerned, and I was fortunate that Edith T. Miller helped me with the lists and with the chapter on miniatures. I am equally grateful to the other prominent and expert dealers who assisted with the lists: Kathryn

Hoffmaster of Pennsylvania; Morris Scott of Indiana; Sonia Bob of New York; my old friend, Jeanne Smith of Geneva, Illinois, (who started me on this blue path many years ago); Sylvia Badt of Michigan, who sent her prices and loaned me the longed-for Singan, and certainly Lois Tucker of Maine, who not only helped with the difficult work of evaluation but who out of her sound experience and background taught me so much about the Mulberry patterns that are catalogued herein.

Write when you feel like doing so, I enjoy your letters and you are always teaching me something. I will try to respond, but if I cannot, please know that I thank all of you from my heart. Your visits and correspondence are vitally interesting and important to me. I feel that you are my friends and that we are involved in a mutual adventure which embraces mystery, detection, surprise and reward.

Until we meet again through letters or in person, or if need be only in the pages of my books, let us say with the Bible (in Genesis), " 'Mizpah'. The Lord watch between thee and me, when we are absent one from the other."

Petra Williams

Jeffersontown, Kentucky
October, 1974

iv

CONTENTS

Page

FLOW BLUE PATTERNS 1

    ORIENTAL CATEGORY 3

    SCENIC CATEGORY 13

    FLORAL CATEGORY 23

    ART NOUVEAU CATEGORY 39

    BRUSH STROKE CATEGORY 43

    MISCELLANEOUS CATEGORY 47

NOTES ON MINIATURE DISHES 67

PRICING PROCEDURES 71

    BUYING 71

    SELLING 75

    UNDERSTANDING THE FLOW BLUE PRICE GUIDES 79

VALUE GUIDES 83

    STONEWARE 83

    LATE VICTORIAN PATTERNS 87

    LATE VICTORIAN MISCELLANY 89

    ART NOUVEAU 91

    NOVELTIES 92

FLOW BLUE INDEX KEYED TO THE VALUE GUIDES 94

HISTORY OF MULBERRY WARE 131

A COMPENDIUM OF MULBERRY WARE PATTERNS 135

INDEX 195

FLOW BLUE CHINA PATTERNS

A SUPPLEMENT

TO

Flow Blue China
An Aid to Identifiction

AND

Flow Blue China II

The dating system used in this book is the same as that employed in the first two books on the subject by the author, and applies to both Flow Blue China and Mulberry Ware patterns. E.V. denotes the Early Victorian period 1835 to 1855-60, M.V. applies to the Middle Victorian era 1860's and 70's, and L.V., the Late Victorian years from the 1880's through the early 1900's. It must be realized by the reader that it is often not possible to date a pattern exactly, therefore the letter "C", which means circa (Latin, and translates as around or about, and is used especially in approximating dates), is used, and in the context of this book, means within about five years before or after the date given.

The Mark numbers that follow the pottery names refer to the numbers assigned by Mr. Geoffrey Godden to the various potters marks in his "Encyclopedia of British Pottery and Porcelain Marks".

**PEPPER POT
AMOY BY DAVENPORT
COLLECTION OF LOIS TUCKER**

Oriental Category

ARABIA
Made by Dawson & Co.

The rim of the sauce dish photographed is fluted, and its edge is accented by a dark line. A garland of small flowers is placed around the rim so as to form large scallops. Bouquets of peonies and poppies alternate with a pair of crossed plumes in the arches made by the garland.

The central scene appears to be Arabian, and because the title on the backstamp is illegible we will use 'ARABIA' until the right name is found. On a terrace contained by a balustrade at right there are two people in robes. A man stands beside a reclining woman. He is dressed in a large turban and dark robe and leans with one hand against the trunk of a tree. The woman is dressed in a light gown with full sleeves and reclines against dark rounded pillows. In the distance at left there are domed buildings and minarets and in the foreground there are a pair of flowers and leaves.

English, marked as above, Mk. 1208, E.V., c. 1845.

CHINESE BOUQUET
Made by W. T. Copeland & Sons

Three diaper designs have been used on the rim of this plate. These are separated by panels of stylized asters on a dark ground. The well is encircled by a spearpoint pattern. The printing has been done in a greyish blue. The pattern almost covers the well. A tall vase at the right is filled with blossoms and slender curving tree branches. The center ground of the main design is filled with a trellis and fence design.

English, marked as above, Mk. 1075, L.V., dated 1884.

CHINESE SPORTS

Possibly made by Jacob Furnival & Company

Entertainers in fanciful costumes are portrayed doing acrobatics on this child's plate. One at the left is standing on his hands and the other is hopping and holding a cymbal in each hand. A tall tree is placed behind the dancing figure and in the distance at left behind stone walls there are a small boat, a tall pagoda and towers. The rim is covered with a diaper pattern of lattice work and dark diamonds.

English, marked impressed "Real Ironstone", E.V., c. 1850.

COREY HILL

Maker Unknown

Three peonies set on a dark ground within large foliated scrolls separate the three scenic panels on the rim of this plate. The scenes depict a large two storied pagoda, a fence, tree and bushes. These are set upon symbolic rock forms which are painted black. Small flowers and stems form a garland tracery around the well. The center scene shows a small vase on a table which surmounts a small scroll and some rock forms. An overscaled flower is at left and the garland tracery is used again around the central motif. Colors of henna, grey, blue and black have been heavily applied on this example.

This is probably E.V., c. 1845.

HIZEN

Made by G. L. Ashworth & Brothers

A scrawling oriental floral pattern covers this gold edged plate. A gnarled bough circles the plate and connects the overscaled flowers. A small bird is perched at the top of the well.

English, marked A. Bros. and impressed Ashworth, Mk. 141, M.V., c. 1870

HYSON

Made by Joseph Clementson

This plate is unevenly scalloped. The outer one-half inch edge of the rim is raised and is decorated with a dark band contained by scrolls. Four heraldic tassel designs of foliated scrolls, flanked by large leaves, and topped by four-petaled flowers alternate with groups of peonies on the rim. The well is encircled by a brocade band of squares. The central scene shows a pagoda at left. A banner is flying from its tower and at right there is a tea house from which stairs descend to a platform at center where a man is seated smoking a pipe and an attendant is holding a parasol over his head.

English, marked as above, Mk. 910A, E.V., c. 1845.

INDIAN TREE

Maker Unknown

This two handled tyg is decorated with a tree of life pattern which shows branches and exotic flowers. This pattern was derived from designs conceived in India. In the example photographed the transfer print is flown cobalt and the flowers and leaves are overpainted with henna red, light green and bright gold.

Probably English and probably E.V., c. 1845.

MANILA

Probably made by J. Ridgway
or Samuel Alcock

This is the same center pattern as Lahore by Corn shown in Book I, page 35. The border is different and consists of four reserves formed by double scallops which surround a heart form set in a triangle formed by Gothic scrolls. In each reserve there is a scene of a temple flanked by a tree at the left and a small pavilion at the right.

English, marked with the early English Coat of Arms, E.V., c. 1845.

MEDALLION

Made by Brown, Westhead, Moore & Co.

Slate blue was used to print the pattern on this compote. The design title was bestowed because of the oval medallions outlined in blackish blue that are placed on the rim. These are separated by stylized prunus. The outer edge is outlined by a narrow border of diamond diapering and this is repeated in the band that encircles the well which is covered with large sprawling of peonies, dahlias, leaves and stems.

English, marked B. W. M. Co., Like Mk. 676, L.V., c. 1900.

MEMPHIS

Maker Unknown

Very small scallops form the edge of this plate, and the gilded outer edge is detailed with a band of crosshatching contained within embossed small scallops. The plate is decorated with a "Japan" pattern on the rim. Foliated scrolls form a horizontal pattern that separates reserves which contain large dahlias, stems, leaves and buds. An angular vase is placed at the right center of the well and it is filled with overscaled flowers, leaves and sprigs. Flowers and leaves are placed at its base. Two sections of fence are placed to the left and there are two small urns placed on the fence posts. A tall hollyhock type plant finishes the design at the extreme left.

Probably English, E.V., c. 1845.

MINTON JAPAN

Made by Minton

The rim of this unevenly scalloped plate is divided into four sections by dark scrolls that form arched reserves and are joined by a double ring placed over a scrolled base that enters the well. There are different oriental floral groups in each reserve. A diapered background appears on the upper rim above the dark scrolls.

In the center an oblong basket form is filled with peony blossoms, wisteria and prunus. Adjoining the basket in the foreground there is a large dahlia with leaves. Many colours have been used over the transfer on this plate, but the scrolls, leaves and basket are cobalt.

There is no title on the backstamp, this name is used to catalogue.

English, marked B. B. (Best Body), "New Stone" and dated E.V., c. 1846.

NANKIN

Possibly made by Wood & Brownfield

This is a good example of Chinoiserie. The drawing is fanciful and not at all realistic. The central scene depicts a man who is standing on a scrolled platform at the left. He is holding an open parasol over his shoulder. Flowers and a large garland link his perch to a grassy flower strewn bank at the right. In the center ground a small seated figure is fishing from the right bank of a stream and in the background there are some islands and a boat.

English, marked W. & B., Mk 4242, E.V., c. 1850.

NAPIER
Made by J & G Alcock

The two twelve-sided cup plates photographed show how different items in the same pattern can appear. Each has the same outer edge of herringbone pattern and each has a rim division design of flowers and geometric rock design. The scenic reserves on the rim contain a tall pagoda with a willow tree at the right and a boat in the distance. On one plate the central scene shows only a large boat in the centerground on which there are a person carrying a fringed parasol and another figure, a woman, who is standing and holding a child by the hand; the child is scooping water out of the river with a dish. A tall willow tree is at right and there are islands in the background. The other plate pictures the boat and the people in it at left center, islands in the background and a long fence across the foreground. At the right there are two large figures and one small one on a platform. The one at right seems to be an attendant in a peaked hat who holds a fringed parasol over the head of an elaborately gowned woman, who holds a child by the hand.

English, marked J. & G. A. & "Imperial Stone" Mk. 69A E.V., c. 1842.

RORSTRAND'S ORIENTAL
Made by Rorstrand

The dish pictured is the bottom of a vegetable serving vessel. The border design consists of foliated triangular reserves that alternate with horizontal open spaces carrying stylized dahlias, lotus flowers and leaves. The center design is dominated by a tall slender flowering tree at left. At its base there is a small garden house. Three figures appear on a platform at center. One leans on a pole. At the right center at a distance there are pagodas and mountains. The center scene is the same as that used by T. and T. J. Meyer on Formosa.

This is probably Swedish, it is marked as above. Rorstrand is a pottery near Stockholm. See Thorn, page 113, Mk. 3, M.V., c. 1880.

SICILIAN

Made by J. T. Close & Co.

There is no title on the backstamp so we will use this name to catalogue the pattern. Tinghai was a town on the island of Chusan.

The bowls pictured are part of a nest of bowls. The edge is decorated with a row of heavy embossed beads. The rim is decorated with large foliated scrolled cartouches that contain oriental flowers and leafy sprigs. These are set upon a background of fish scale diapering and small flowers. Large scrolls contain the patterns at the top edge.

The central scene on one of the set shows a Chinoiserie gateway at the left center in which a small robed figure is standing. Tall trees and overscaled flowers are placed at the top of three flat steps at the right.

On the other two bowls the central scene portrays a gazebo with very fancy roof at the left. A large flower filled urn stands on a pedestal in front of the garden house and in the center of the picture a large overscaled flower is placed in the foreground. At the right there is a Gothic (!) tower and behind that there are tall peaked mountains.

English, marked J. T. Close and Stoneware Staffordshire, E.V., c. 1855.

SUNFLOWERS
Maker Unknown

A tall bamboolike stalk rises from the left part of the base of this pitcher. There are two overscaled exotic flowers near the stalk, and many sunflowers on both sides of the main branch and at the top which arches over the center of the vessel. Two stylized crested pheasants are placed in the right foreground.

The border design is composed of heavily scrolled cartouches that contain one-half of a sunflower. The dominant motif can be found in the half sunflower design, which separates the scrolled reserves. This half flower is placed over a large round bead and tassel, and is flanked by leaf forms. There is no backstamp on the base, this name is used to present the pattern.

Probably English or Dutch, E.V. or M.V.

SYLVIA
Made by Joseph Clementson

The plate photographed is decorated half way down the rim with stylized flowers and scrolls. The medallion in the center of the plate is outlined with a band of brocade, which is interrupted by butterfly forms at six points. In the center of the medallion there is a stylized flower set upon a scroll and a bird is perched upon the flower. This is probably a representation of the Asiatic Pheasant motif as the bird is crested and has long curved tailfeathers.

English, marked as above, impressed "ironstone", Mk. 910A, E.V., c. 1850.

TYG

Maker Unknown

The border of this pattern is not shown as it was placed on the inside top of the mug. It consists of diamond treillage which dips in deep scallops. Inside each scallop there is a five petaled flower. In the scrolled arches formed between the scallops there is a small sprig at the top and a garland below.

The scene differs on the two sides of the tyg. One shows a man fishing from a garden house at left which is approached by a fenced staircase. A tall tree arches over the center of the scene. In the foreground there is part of a fence and an overscaled flower. In the background at right there are a house and a large junk with sails. The other side of the mug is dominated by a peaked-roofed house in the center. This is placed on a terrace and there is a smaller building at right. The branches of a tall prunus tree are above the houses. At the left there is an urn filled with willow branches set next to rock forms. In the left background there are a house and three pine trees.

Probably English, probably E.V. or M.V.

WHAMPOA

Made by Samuel Keeling & Co.

This scalloped plate bears a rim design of large foliated scrolls the tips of which enter the well and form a leafy wreath.

The central scene show three figures in oriental garb. A man, holding a pole over his shoulder with one hand and a small child with the other stand at the left. They are watching another child who wears a coolie hat play with a hoop. A tall tree is behind the second child and there are fields and a towered building in the background.

English, marked S. K. & Co., Mk. 2247, E.V., c. 1845.

Scenic Category

CASTLE

Made by John Tams

The collar, lid and base of this sugar bowl are decorated with large curling foliated scrolls that alternate with a geometric design of three pendants composed of diamonds.

The scene on the body depicts parts of a ruined stone castle. A round tower with domed top is in the center of the scene. It is connected to an arch form at left by a narrow pointed arch door with a Gothic overhead. In the left foreground there are the remains of a large arched bridge that crosses a moat. Tall trees and heavy bushes obscure most of the details of the building.

English, marked J. T., Mk. 3791, M.V., c. 1875.

CHELSEA

Made by Bishop & Stonier

The pitcher photographed is one of a set of three milk pitchers which are 7-1/8 inches, 8 inches and 8-3/4 inches high. These pitchers are typical of this era. The scene on the pitcher photographed is hard to distinguish but it appears to depict a hill on which there are classic buildings and trees. In the foreground there may be water, but a white path clearly goes from the foreground to the hill.

The scene is set within a Gothic arch surmounted by stylized Art Nouveau flowers.

English, marked B. & S., Mk. 384, L.V., c. 1900.

14

COLUMBIAN STAR
Made by John Ridgway

This scenic plaque bears no title so the name above is given in order to present the pattern.

The gold edged plate is covered with a scene typical of the days of the taming of the land beyond Cumberland Mountains. A man plows his land, the logs of the trees he has felled are in the foreground. In the center there is a log cabin with smoke curling from its stone chimney. A woman and child sit on a bench in front of the front door. In the distance a flag waves from a tall pole set on a promontory in a river. Tall trees complete the design.

English, marked as above, impressed and dated E.V., 1840.

COTTAGE
Made by John & Robert Godwin

The rim of this deep saucer is divided into sixteen panels and is decorated with a design of a single flower set in a foliated oblong cartouche. This alternates with a small shield set between scrolls and filled with treillage. The center scene is bucolic. It shows a thatched house with two tall chimneys. A lean-to is attached at its left side. Tall trees are placed on both the right and left background and in the foreground a pair of cows are grazing behind part of a fence and some bushes.

English, marked J. & R. G., Mk. 1726, E.V., c. 1850.

FLENSBURG

Possibly made by James Edwards

The rim of this twelve sided deep dish is covered with an outer wreath of very dark foliated scrolls, and an inner circle of light blue small leaves.

The center design was printed in cobalt and then other colors were used, so that the plate is polychrome. At the left a Prussian eagle with wings outstretched and head turned to the right (facing) sits on top of a two handled urn. An overscaled rose is at the base of the urn and an equally large lily and stem are at the right. Delicate willow branches and sprigs serve as background.

Flensburg is in Germany and is located near the border of Denmark. The city passed from the Danish crown to Prussia in 1865, and it is possible that this pattern was printed to commemorate that event.

English, marked "Warranted", (impressed), E.V., c. 1865.

"IN THE BUNKER"

Maker Unknown

The above title appears on the base of the vase photographed. The scene includes a golfer in knickerbockers who is hitting his way out of a sand trap. Two caddies, holding bags full of clubs, stand and watch the shot.

Probably English, probably L.V., c. 1905.

THE MANOR

Maker Unknown

The basketweave edge of this bowl slants downward from the edge of the dish.

The scene consists of a large house at the left behind a tall elm tree. An arched bridge crosses a stream at the center and there are two swans on the water in the foreground. The bank at right is covered with overscaled dahlias and peonies, and a tall tree is placed behind the flowers. In the distance there are Alpine peaks.

There is no backstamp on this shallow bowl. This name is used to present both the interesting mold and the scenic pattern.

Probably English, probably M.V.

MONTEREY

Made by Joseph Heath

The rim of this deep saucer is decorated with five reserves containing a picture of a building and towers flanked by trees. Two people are silhouetted at right. The reserves are divided by Gothic scrolls that form a diamond set against concentric lines. The printing is done in slate blue. A circle of oblongs centered with a tiny square point wreaths the well.

The scene in the center is the usual romantic European picture of a large castle like building that is placed at the left and which is set against a backdrop of Alpine peaks. There are tall elms at the right and in the foreground there is a balustrade at left topped by two statues, and another balustrade at right. Four persons are in the foreground on a grassy bank of the river that divides the scene. A full moon shines over the scene.

English, marked J. Heath, Mk. 1993, E.V., c. 1850

MOSELLE
Made by E. Wood

This plate is fourteen sided and paneled. On the rim a Gothic design of scrolls and foliated shields is contained at the outer edge by a row of printed beads. Double swags of flowers are placed between the shield forms. The landscape in the center depicts the buildings and trees to be found along the bank of the Moselle River, which flows into the Rhine. A castle with a round tower is at right, a tall graceful tree at left, and a narrow bridge crosses the water at center. In the foreground there are two mooring poles.

English, marked as above, marked Kaolin Ware, mark not found. E.V., c. 1846.

PERCY
Made by Francis Morley

The printing on this saucer is done in a greyish blue that has a lavender cast. Its outer edge is encircled by a ribbon that appears against a pebbled background. The rim is decorated with delicate sprigs of small flowers and the well is detailed by a wreath of floral sprigs. The central scene depicts a chalet on the left. It is behind the ruins of a bridge composed of tall stone arches and is surmounted by a tall pole from which a pennant flies. There are a village and mountains in the distance.

English, mark (imp.) F. M., Mk. 2759, E.V., c. 1850.

**SOUVENIR,
CHAUTAUQUA, NEW YORK**

**SOUVENIR,
OLD ORCHARD BEACH, MAINE**

**SOUVENIR,
PORT ARTHUR, TEXAS**

Made by Wheelock

These plates are printed in slate blue. The outer edge is detailed by a row of flowers and stems. The six scenes shown on each are framed in foliated scrolls and violets. The titles appear at the bottom on a ribbon.

English, marked as above, mark not found, L.V., c. 1910.

STORK
Made by John Tams

The edge of this fluted plate is covered with gold lustre. The dish is covered with a picture of a stork standing on one leg in a stream of water. He is surrounded by tall reeds, lilies and elongated leaves. A large frog is perched on a lily pad in front of the bird and an overscaled winged insect flies overhead.

English, marked as above with "Longton", dated, Mk. 879, L.V., c. 1880.

TIVOLI
Made by Charles Meigh

A twelve sided cup plate is photographed. The rim is encircled by concentric lines; wild roses with large ivy leaves and stems surround the outer edge. A wreath of ivy leaves, buds and thick stems surround the upper part of the well. The center scene is the usual romantic picture. There are tall elms at the left and a castle like building appears on a hill at the right background. There is a ruin in the left background. A river is seen in the middle and three people are on a bank in the foreground.

English, marked as above, and (imp.) Improved Stone China, Mk. 2618, E.V., c. 1845.

TURKEY
Made by Cauldon, Ltd.

The plate photographed is unevenly scalloped and the edge is detailed with a row of little flowers and leaves. The design is printed in a dark slate blue and on the rim appears as four large designs composed of foliated scrolls. In the space between these there are pictures of different game birds in flight. The center design on the plate presents a large turkey gobbler with his feathers puffed out. He is standing in the midst of tall grass and weeds.

English, marked as above, Mk. 821, L.V., c. 1905.

VINCENNES
Made by John Alcock

The details of the pattern as shown on this cup plate are difficult to discern so another picture of a larger plate in mulberry is included. Note that no bridge appears on the cup plate. The rims of both plates are decorated with three scenic cartouches containing a columned temple. These alternate with three reserves that are centered with a small bouquet. The dark background spaces between these resemble keyholes and are topped at the outer edge with a quatrefoil and a foliated flame design. A row of spear point encircles the well. The central scene is the usual romantic Victorian landscape. A tall elm rises from a river bank at the right and behind it there are square towers. At the left rear there are castle buildings. In the foreground there is a small tree at left and two persons are on the bank in the center. The pattern is distinguished by a bridge of many arches that crosses the river in the middle of the picture.

English, marked as above, with Cobridge, Mk. 67, E.V., c. 1857.

Actual Size
3" Wide, 3" High

RECIPE FOR SYLLABUB

"Put a pint and a half of port or white wine into a bowl, nutmeg grated, and a good deal of sugar, then milk into it near 2 quarts of milk, frothed up. If the wine be not rather sharp it will require more for this quantity of milk. Clouted cream may be put on the top, and pounded cinnamon and sugar."

From Mary Randolph's "The Virginia Housewife or Methodical Cook" 1831.

Clouted cream was made by heating together beaten eggs, milk, rosewater and mace, then removing the top when the mixture had cooled overnight.

RECIPE FOR SACK POSSET

"Take four ounces of pounded sugar, a pint of sherry and some grated nutmeg; warm them over the fire until the sugar is dissolved; then beat up ten fresh eggs, and strain them into a quart of new milk that has been boiled (but stood until cool), and add the wine and sugar, put the whole in to a clean sauce pan on the fire, and keep stirring until it is nearly boiled, then remove, or it will curdle."

From "Indian Domestic Economy and Receipt Book" 1849.

RECIPE FOR CUSTARD POSSET

"Take fourteen Eggs, beat them very well, and put to them twelve spoonfulls of Sack, nine of Ale, and half a Pound of Sugar. Set them upon some coals and warm them, then strain them, and set them on again, and heat beat them until they begin to thicken; and if you please, you may add a little nutmeg. Take one Quart of Cream and boil it, pour it into the Eggs, cover it up and let it stand half an hour; then serve it up."

From Mrs. Martha Bradley's "British Housewife".

Floral Category

ALTHEA

Probably made by Podmore, Walker & Co.

The edge of this gently scalloped platter is embossed with a deep ridged band and leaves, which are covered with dark cobalt. The center of the platter is covered with a large design of Althea blossoms and leaves. Althea is the botanical name for hollyhock.

English, marked "Pearl" and an impressed rosette, E.V., c. 1850.

ANEMONE

Probably made by Hollinshead & Kirkham

The base of the gravy tureen shown is covered with a sprawling design of windflowers and leaves, but the lid has anemones on one side only. The side shown bears a large full blown rose.

English, marked H. & K., probably mark 2071, L.V., c. 1880.

ANEMONE

Made by Villeroy & Boch

The rim of this unevenly scalloped dish is covered with a baroque design of treillage alternating with wild and cultivated roses which are placed against very dark scrolled triangular reserves. The center design consists of a single anemone with leaves and buds.

German, marked V. & B., Mk. 40, page 37, Thorn, L.V., c. 1900.

24

ANGELUS (THE)

Made by Homer Laughlin China Company

This bone dish is scalloped and gilt edged. A very dark band forms the background for sprays of small anemones, leaves and stems. Dark scrolls are placed on the bottom of the design and trailing forget-me-nots enter the well which is bordered by a band of gold spearpoint.

This dish was given to the museum and although the background is blue it may be borderline.

American, marked as above, See Thorn, page 133, Mk. 28, L.V., c. 1880.

BONITA

Made by Wheeling Pottery Company

This is the La Belle pattern as shown in Book I, page 109. The gilded edge of this plate is irregularly scalloped. An asymmetrical pattern of small flowers is placed on the rim. This consists of two small sprays that are placed opposite a sprawling arrangement of the same flowers. The design covers half the rim and extends to the center of the well.

American, marked as above, L.V., c. 1900.

BURLINGTON

Made by Wedgwood & Co. Ltd.

The outer scalloped edge of this plate is defined by a dark slate blue stippled band which is contained by rococco scrolls. The design appears only on the rim and consists of three water lilies set in scrolled reserves and paired with a full blown rose and buds. These are separated by pairs of lilies, small flowers and sprigs which enter the well.

English, marked as above, Mk. 4059, L.V., c. 1906.

CAMELLIA

Made by Wedgwood & Co., Ltd.

The vessel photographed is probably the bottom of a covered vegetable dish. It is irregularly scalloped and the edge is embossed with a raised ridge interrupted by raised leaves. The baroque rim pattern features scrolled reserves, three of which contain a single camellia with leaves and buds. The alternating three contain a triangular scroll design topped with a fleur-de-lis. A band of narrow scrolls circles the well. The large central design is composed of two ruffled camellias with leaves and small sprays of prunus.

English, marked as above, (imp.) Mk. 4075, probably M.V.

CARNATION

Made by Mintons

The platter photographed is unevenly scalloped and the edge is detailed with a cobalt band.

Eight large flowers of varied species, tulip, rose, anemone, daffodil and others are placed around the rim. The bouquet in the center is composed principally of carnations, which are flanked with small flowers and sprigs.

English, marked B. B. and dated Mk. 2705, E.V.

COREA

Made by Wedgwood & Co., Ltd.

This scalloped plate has a very dark band printed over the embossing around the edge. The rim is decorated with two groups of peonies and small flowers that are placed opposite each other. The design is composed basically of four floral groups. Two, that face each other, are formed around a triangular scrolled cartouche that contains a small stylized flower, and which is flanked by realistic dahlias and daisies; these alternate with the peonies, and are separated from them by oval pendants. The bottoms of the four large designs enter the well.

English, marked as above, Mk. 4057, L.V., c. 1900.

CRANSTON

Made by Burgess & Leigh

The edge of this plate is scalloped and gilded. The design appears on the rim and enters the well at three points. The pattern is somewhat asymmetrical as it covers one-half of the rim more thickly than the other side, and consists of trailing ivy leaves and small blossoms. (This name is used to catalogue. The back stamp is illegible after "Cranes").

English, Registry #191312, marked as above, Mk. 717, L.V., c. 1910.

DELAWARE

Made by J. & G. Meakin

The edge of this deeply scalloped and embossed plate is decorated with a heavy band of scrolls. These form triangles at five points which point to the well. There are sprays, consisting of daisies and a full blown rose, between the triangular designs.

English, marked as above, Like Mk. 2601, L.V., c. 1890.

27

FLORA

Made by Davenport

The rim of this white edged plate is divided into four sections by ribbon-like wide bands. The spaces between the bands are filled with sprays of small flowers and leaves. The bottom of both designs enters the well and effects a wreath.

The well is almost covered with a bouquet of large roses and other flowers placed in and around a basket with a ribbon bow on its handle. A butterfly is placed at top center on the handle.

There is no title on the back stamp, this name is given in order to present the pattern.

English, marked as above (imp.), dated January 8th, 1850, E.V., c. 1850.

FLORENTINE

Made by Thomas Dimmock

This design is composed of large baroque scrolls which are placed around the rim of the plate as connections between sprays of various flowers, roses, camellias, peonies and carnations.

English, marked D. & Kaolin Ware, Mk. 1298, E.V., c. 1844.

FRUIT AND FLOWERS

Made by Doulton & Co.

The edge of this gently scalloped plate is bordered with a row of large beads. The rim is covered with a design of large fruits, such as peaches and figs with leaves, set against a dark background. These alternate with reserves containing flowers. The center of the plate is almost covered by a design of overscaled flowers placed in an urn which is placed on the top left of a brick wall. Some trees and bushes can be seen at right beyond the wall. There is no title on the back, this name is used to catalogue.

English, marked Royal Doulton, Mk. 1333, dated May, 1904, L.V., c. 1904.

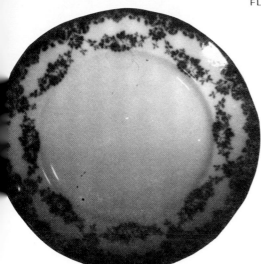

GARLAND

Made by The Albion Pottery
(Bourne & Leigh, Ltd.)

Garlands of roses printed in a slate blue are joined by a large rose and a bow on the rim of the plate photographed. The gilded outer edge is encircled by a band of very dark blue, contained by scrolls printed in a much lighter tone.

English, marked E. B. & J. E. L., Mk. 486, L.V., c. 1910.

GERANEUM

Made by Podmore, Walker & Company

The rim of this plate is printed with a wreath of Geraniums, flowers, leaves and buds. A print of two large blossoms and leaves is placed across the well.

English, marked P. W. & Company, Mk. 3075, E.V., c. 1845.

GROSVENOR

Made by Charles Meigh & Son

This scalloped plate is gilt edged. Only the leaves and the pattern are done in cobalt blue that has been allowed to flow into the surrounding area. The rest of the pattern is printed in many colours. The pattern may be considered borderline but seems to be an experiment by Meigh. The pattern has been mentioned for many years as a flow blue pattern and is included here for reference. It may also have been made in plain flow blue cobalt without the other colors that are applied here over the floral parts of the pattern.

English, marked C. M. & S., Like Mk. 2620, E.V., c. 1855.

IPOMOEA

Made by Charles Meigh & Son

The article photographed is a round stand for a tureen. The open work handles are fitted to the plate with heavy scroll embossing. Five pairs of baroque scrolls are placed around the edge and a ribbon band defines the design at the outer edge. In the space between the scrolls where an arch is formed at the apex of the touching scrolls a reserve is formed and in these reserves there are placed morning glories and leaves. The central medallion is composed of a single morning glory surrounded by a ribbon like that around the outer edge, and this is decorated with five fleur-de-lis.

Ipomoea is the botanical name for morning glory.

English, marked C. M. & S. and Improved Stone China. Like Mk. 2620, E.V., c. 1851.

IRIS

Made by W. E. Corn

This serving dish is deeply scalloped and the upper part of the rim is heavily embossed and gives a shell effect. A dark blue band enhances the outer edge. The asymmetrical design of large iris and leaves curves part way around the well.

English, marked as above, Mk. 1112, L.V., c. 1900.

JOSEPHINE

Made by Ridgways

This scalloped plate has the heavy gadroon edge featured by Ridgways. The very dark rim pattern consists of four full blown roses, leaves and forget-me-nots. The pattern invades the well and is confined by a wreath of small stylized lily shapes.

English, marked as above, Mk. 3313, L.V., c. 1910.

LILY

Made by W. Adams & Sons

The plate photographed is scalloped, gilt edged and embossed with beading and bow knots. The pattern appears on the rim and consists of large water lilies and pads connected by lily buds and swirling stems. The veins and outlines of the flowers are enhanced with gold paint.

English, marked as above, Mk. 22, M.V., c. 1860.

LOUISE

Made by John Maddock & Sons

The edge of this gilded scalloped wash basin is outlined in blue. Two large triangular groups formed of asters, leaves and sprigs face each other across the body of the vessel and two small horizontal sprays are placed between them. Gold lustre has been placed over the flowers and around the edge.

English, marked as above, Mk. 2463, L.V., c. 1891.

MOSS ROSE

Made by John Ridgway

The mold used for this plate is unusual. The rim is divided into six large embossed curved scallops, divided by six small embossed crown shapes, each detailed by three oval beads. The edge is outlined in blue over the embossing and small garlands are placed beneath the crown shapes. The entire well is covered by a print of one large full blown rose, its leaves and buds and two sprays of fern.

English, marked I. Ridgway, Mk. 3256 and 3257, dated October 2, 1847, E.V., c. 1847.

MOW COP

Made by Brown, Westhead, Moore Company

The pattern on this plate appears on the rim, although a few sprigs enter the well. The design consists of pansies printed in a greyish blue. These are placed at three points on the rim and are connected by sprays of forget-me-nots.

English, marked as above, Registry #70235, Mk. 679, M.V., c. 1862.

NELSON

Made by New Wharf Pottery

This dish is scalloped and embossed with scrolls and small flowers around the outer edge. The pattern appears on the rim and consists of five horseshoe shapes composed of flowers and sprays that alternate with sprigs of small daisies that are flanked by vertical scroll embossing.

English, marked N. W. P., Mk. 2886, L.V., c. 1890.

PETUNIA

Made by Cumberlidge & Humphreys

The small covered biscuit jar pictured bears a large design of petunias on its rounded fluted body. The collar is dark blue, gilt edged and scalloped. A smaller design appears with sprigs on the lid and gold lustre has been placed around the edge of the vessel.

English, marked C. & H., and Tunstall, Mk. 1158, L.V., c. 1893.

PHOEBE

Made by Wedgwood & Company, Ltd.

The dish photographed is unevenly scalloped and is gilt edged. The pattern, printed in slate blue, appears on the rim and consists of three (possibly four on a large flat plate) cartouches that contain a bouquet. The long spaces between are filled with sprigs and the outer edge is bordered with a band of flame like designs. A dark band containing lighter horizontal scallops encircles the well and inside this there is a row of spear point composed of darts and beads.

English, marked as above, Mk. 4059, L.V., c. 1906.

POMONA

Made by Ridgways

This punch bowl is covered with small blossoms and leaves. The pattern resembles "Astoria" by Upper Hanley Pottery and "Hawthorne" by Mercer Pottery Company and may be the same. It also resembles the famous designs of prunus blossoms used by the Chinese.

English, marked as above, Mk. 3312, L.V., c. 1910.

POPPY

Made by Charles Meigh & Son

The surface of a footed dish is shown. The design was printed in cobalt which was allowed to flow, then colours were added over the blue pattern. The poppies in the center are coloured red and burnt orange. The leaves and the stems are in cobalt highlighted with gold. Pink, green and yellow also appear on the design. The deep embossed scroll around the edge and the handles are covered with deep cobalt and trimmed with gold.

English, marked C. M. & S., Mk. 2620, E.V., c. 1855.

POPPY
Made by Thomas Till & Son

Slate blue has been used to print the sprawling design of poppies, stems and leaves that covers the body of the pitcher photographed. The same pattern is used predominantly on one side of the matching basin.

English, marked as above, Mk. 3858, L.V., c. 1880.

POPPY
Maker Unknown

The rim of this small platter is fluted and its edge is outlined with dark blue. Three different renditions of a pair of poppies, leaves and buds are placed around the rim and across the upper part of the well.

Probably English, L.V., c. 1900.

PRUNUS
Maker Unknown

This round tray is large (13 inches) and is probably the stand for a tureen. The dark scalloped outer edge is marked by raised embossing which is interrupted at four points with embossed leaves. It is very similar to the mold used by Wood & Baggaly, as seen in other flow blue patterns, principally "Ambrosia" and "Windsor Wreath". The rather stylized pattern of prunus blossoms, leaves and stems covers the entire dish.

There is no back stamp on this example. The name "Prunus" is given in order to present the pattern.

It is probably English and probably M.V., c. 1870.

QUEEN

Made by Ford and Son

The pitcher and basin photographed are decorated with large full blown roses and leaves. The edge of the basin and the top of the pitcher are scalloped and detailed with a dark floral band that is gilt edged.

English, marked F. & S., with Burslem, Mk. 1583, L.V., c. 1900.

RHODA

Made by William Adams & Son

The pattern on this scalloped plate appears only on the rim and consists of a wreath of flowers bound together by sprigs and scrolls. Dainty embossing outlines the outer edge and also encircles the well at the bottom of the rim.

English, marked as above, Mk. 28, L.V., c. 1891.

ROSE SPRAYS

Made by William Adams & Son

This unevenly scalloped relish dish is printed in a slate blue. Its outer edge is dark and is defined by a row of embossed beading. The pattern is asymmetrical and consists of a large spray of roses on one side and a single rose and small bouquet on the opposite side.

English, marked as above, Mk. 30, L.V., c. 1910.

RUSTIC

Made by W. H. Grindley

The creamer and sugar bowl pictured carry a slate blue design of sprawling branches and buds, that appear to be wild flowers.

English, marked as above, Mk. 1842, L.V., c. 1891.

SPRINGFIELD

Made by Alfred Meakin, Ltd.

The edge of this plate is scalloped and embossed with small flowers. The design is printed in greyish blue. The rim pattern consists of pairs of wild roses interspersed with small forget-me-nots and other little flowers. A wreath of forget-me-nots circles the inside of the well.

English, marked as above, Mk. 2586, L.V., c. 1891.

SUHRNGLEN

Made by Ridgways

The square butter pat photographed bears the title name in German script. The dish is gently scalloped and is gilt edged. A ribbon band of small ovals containing flowers outlines the deep rim. Pairs of small flowers are placed on each side of the dish. On the larger round plate of this set the flowers are probably connected by a wreath of sprigs.

English, (may have been made for German Trade.) Marked as above, Registry #7222, Mk. 3310, M.V., c. 1884.

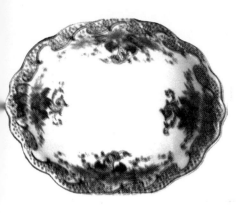

SYBIL

Made by Henry Alcock & Co., Ltd.

The design on this basin is printed in slate blue. The outer edge is scalloped and is outlined by a small row of forget-me-nots and embossed large four-petal flowers that are overprinted. Scrolls are used to contain the border design. The four inner sides of the basin are printed with large flowers that resemble poinsettias. These are set in cornucopias composed of scrolls and decorated with the same small flowers that rim the edge.

English, marked as above, Mk. 65, E.V., c. 1910.

WATER LILY

Made by W. T. Copeland

This unevenly scalloped dish is bordered with a blue spear point pattern that is interrupted at six points by a pair of small flowers. A row of similar spear point encircles the well. A large scale drawing of water lilies and leaves covers the well.

English, marked Copeland, Late Spode, Mk. 1068, dated 1850, E.V., c. 1850.

Art Nouveau Category

ANGLESEA
Made by J. G. Meakin

The plates in this pattern are unevenly scalloped and the edges are trimmed with gold. The pattern consists of three narrow lines that encircle the outer edge. From the innermost line a geometric design consisting of triangles that enclose three pointed arrows points toward the well. This alternates with a large pattern of five small dark squares from which three large arrows also point towards the well.

This design is closer to the Art Deco Period than to the Art Nouveau.

One plate in this pattern has been found marked "Non-Pareil". It may be a mismarking or it may be another name used for the same design by the same potter.

English, marked as above, Mk. 2603, L.V., c. 1912.

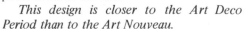

BELMONT
Made by Ford & Son, Ltd.

The dark edge of this dish is unevenly scalloped and is decorated with a band of small printed scallops and dark beads placed over a field of lighter blue. This motif is repeated in the band around the well. The pattern appears only on the rim and consists of a quatrefoil flanked by stylized tulips. These are joined by thin curved lines that intertwine and terminate in leaf forms in the middle of the spaces between the quatrefoils. Three small dotted circles are placed around the leaf designs.

English, marked F. & Sons Burslem, Mk. 1585, L.V., c. 1890.

DEVON
Made by Ford & Son, Ltd.

This plate is unevenly scalloped. The design on the rim consists of five wide heart shaped scrolls with a pair of peonies on either side. These alternate with five heart shaped designs of scrolls under which there is a pair of sprigs that enters the well. The well is encircled by a row of tiny fringe.

We show two pictures in this pattern in order to show the difference between the way the pattern is applied on a square platter and a round plate. On the platter the designs on the sides are elongated and the sprigs in the well are placed within the fringe at the corners of the platter.

English, marked F. & Sons, Ltd., Mk. 1586, L.V., c. 1908.

LUSITANIA
Made by Alfred Colley & Company, Ltd.

This pattern is the same as "Iris" by Arthur J. Wilkinson. See Flow Blue China An Aid to Identification, page 151.

English, marked as above, Mk. 999, L.V., c. 1910.

OCHIS

Made by W.H. Grindley

The edge of this saucer is scalloped and beaded. The rim design consists of stylized vase shapes which alternate with a fan and fleur-de-lis design. Both are flanked by large scrolls. The spaces between the two main designs is filled with stylized leaves, flowers and scrolls from which small sprigs descend into the well.

The central medallion is a pin wheel design of scrolls and sprigs centered with a six pointed star.

English, marked as above, Mk. 1842, L.V., c. 1891.

OXFORD

Made by William Adderly & Company

The swirling design on this scalloped gilt edged saucer is very typical of Art Nouveau. A butterfly effect is gained by placing winglike curves on either side of a stylized flower and this design alternates with a pair of the same flowers placed upon stylized leaves and curving lines that form a vase. The designs are joined by the long curving lines, and elongated sprays of three flowers and leaves are placed around the well.

English, marked W. A. A. & Company, Registry #368266, Mk. 48, L.V., c. 1900.

Brush–Stroke
Painted Category

GAUDY BLUEBELL

The bluebells on the rim and in the center of this plate are painted pale blue. The small berries are painted in a faded red and the other details of the design are in cobalt.

GINGHAM FLOWER

STAR WITH GOTHIC TRIM

TULIP LUSTRE WITH COLORED CIRCLE

This pattern is the same as Lustre Bond shown on page 222 Vol. II, but a narrow blue line is set inside the lustre edging and a narrow red line is set below that. These two colors are used to form a circle in the center.

Miscellaneous Category

ALDINE

Made by W. H. Grindley

The plate photographed is unevenly scalloped and the edge is detailed by an embossed line. There is also delicate embossing of dotted garlands. The design appears on the rim and consists of two wreaths of tiny flowers and buds. One circles the edge the other is placed around the well.

English, marked as above, Registry #325874, Mk. 1842, L.V., c. 1891.

ALPHABET MUG

Maker Unknown

Hand positions for each of the letters of the alphabet are pictured in squares on the sides of this mug. These instructive pictures are for the use of deaf and dumb persons. The printing of the signs is done in sepia brown but the top edge, bottom rim and handle are cobalt and so are the coral twig decorations between the panels. The entire body of the cup is faintly blue.

English, probably M.V. or L.V.

ASIATIC PHEASANTS

Made by Thomas Hughes & Sons

This is another version of the popular pattern. The outer edge design on the plates appears to be the same as that used by Meir, (See Book I, Flow Blue China An Aid to Identification, page 169), but the flowers on the rim are more profuse and varied and so are those used in the central design. The birds are placed opposite to those of Meir and the tailfeathers of the bird at the top left are composed of four strands of plumage.

English, marked as above, Mk. 2121, L.V., c. 1910.

BELMONT

Made by J. H. Weatherby & Sons

The top of a covered dish is pictured. The edge is scalloped and a very dark band runs around the outer edge. Two facing dark triangular groups of flowers placed within foliated scrolls and flanked by stylized daisies on a dark ground terminate in large rose sprigs and leaves that enter the central portion of the dish. On each of the other two sides there is an Art Nouveau vertical design flanked by scrolls and small flowers. These terminate in a daisy and sprigs. A row of beading connects the design.

English, marked J. H. W. & Sons, Mk. 4044, L.V., c. 1892.

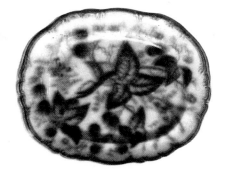

BERRY

Maker Unknown

This unevenly scalloped platter has an embossed edge covered with cobalt. The pattern covers the rim and the well. It consists of large raspberries and leaves set over a shadow tracery of sprigs and buds. A large butterfly is placed at the upper left part of the well, and its twin is located at the lower right part of the well.

English, maker's name illegible, probably E.V.

BRISTOL

Made by Ford & Son

The outer edge of this plate is decorated with a row of inverted hearts. The rim design consists of six teardrop pendants surrounded by floral garlands. These alternate with six stylized groups of roses. The sprigs from these enter the well.

English, marked as above, Mk. 1485, L.V., c. 1905.

CALENDAR PLATE #1

Maker Unknown

The edge of the plate is covered with dark cobalt that fades toward the center. Gold tracery was placed over the blue.

The center scene shows two black swans swimming in a pond near some water lilies. The twelve months of the year 1913 are placed in white circles around the central scene.

This plate is late for this book but is presented along with that of 1915 so that collectors will know such items are available.

Probably American.

CALENDAR PLATE #II

Made by Sterling China Co.

This dish is unevenly scalloped. The top of the rim is covered with cobalt that fades towards the well and gold filigree was placed over the blue.

The central picture shows a map of the Panama Canal area which is surrounded by a wreath composed of the pages of the calendar months for 1915. These are joined at top and bottom by American flags and red and white striped bunting.

This same motif (the building of the Panama Canal) was used on another plate by the Company. See "Panama Canal", this book.

American, marked as above.

CARLTON
Made by Ford & Son

The edge of this unevenly scalloped plate is gilded and is detailed with a printed band of triangular and flame shapes. The garland effect around the rim is created by placing six oval medallions on the rim and separating them with urn shapes composed of scrolls and stylized lily forms placed in a "U" shape of laurel leaves. All are joined together with loops of wild flowers around the upper part of the well.

English, marked F. & Sons and Burslem, Mk. 1585, L.V., c. 1905.

CATHLYN
Made by Ridgways

The pattern of the saucer photographed consists principally of small garlands of bell flowers that are linked to small triangular shell-like forms. The upper circle of garlands is linked by five others placed lower on the rim and which dip into the well.

English, marked as above, Mk. 3313, L.V., c. 1910.

CHINA ASTER
Made by Mintons

The plain unscalloped rim of this plate is decorated with vertical reserves each containing a stylized aster with a straight stem flanked by three leaf forms. The well is covered with a diaper design of snail scrolls on which are superimposed five asters with curved stems. The stems form a rounded cross which is centered with one of the flowers.

English, marked as above, and B. B. Mk. 2713, dated. M.V., c. 1879.

CONSTANCE

Made by William Adderly & Company

Small double sprays of flowers are placed vertically within scroll reserves around the body of this gravy boat. The printing is in a dark slate blue.

English, marked W. A. A. & Co., Mk. 49, Registry #397968, L.V., c. 1902.

DOVER

Made by W. H. Grindley

The plate photographed is unevenly scalloped and the dark edge is embossed with beading.

The design of long reed-like stems topped by daisies appears on the rim against a row of small flowers that form a wreath around the upper rim. The daisies and stems are of different lengths, and some enter the well. A spray of the leaves and flowers is placed in one side of the well.

English, marked as above, Mk. 1842, L.V., c. 1891.

EASTER GREETINGS PREMIUM PLATE

Maker Unknown

The edge of this gilt edged plate is unevenly scalloped and the upper rim is covered with shell and wave embossing, which is covered with dark blue. An octagon was pressed into the mold and this is accented with gold lace filigree on the lower part of the rim.

The central scene shows the snow and ice of winter being melted by the rising sun. At the bottom of the plate the words "Easter Greetings" are printed in gold.

American, L.V., c. 1900.

EASTERN VINES
Made by Charles Meigh

The basin photographed is covered with a sprawling tracery of passion flowers and very dark large stylized leaves and stems. The edge is decorated with a dark line that encloses a row of large oval reserves that contain a medallion centered with a small flower. These are connected by a scroll design. The same pattern is used around the inner top of the basin, and around the top, center of the body and the base, of the matching pitcher.

There is no title given on the backstamp. This name is given to catalogue.

English, marked as above, Mk. 2617 and 2618, E.V., c. 1845.

ECLIPSE
Made by Samuel Alcock & Co.

This plate is underprinted in cobalt blue. Yellow, green and burnt orange have been used over the blue. The rim is covered with a design of six large circles centered with a flower, and these are separated by ovals.

The well is defined by an outer ring of cobalt squares outlined in yellow, and this is repeated in an inner circle.

The central eight pointed medallion is composed of an inner eight pointed star, surrounded by a white circle and eight spear points.

English, marked S. A. & Co., Mk. 75, E.V., c. 1845.

FLORENTINE PATTERN
Made by Pountney and Company

This scalloped, beaded, dark edged soup plate is decorated on the rim with small bouquets in vases. These are joined at the bottom by scrolls and bell flowers that rise to form triangular figures between the vases. Small garlands of sprigs join the two designs and the loops of these enter the well.

English, marked "Bristol" semi-porcelain. Like Mk. 3111, L.V., c. 1889.

GRAND BOUQUET

The edge of this deep dish is bordered in dark blue. Four identical stylized flower sprays are placed on the rim. The central design consists of two curved branches of stylized fruits and flowers joined at the base by a large petaled flower and a triangular design of straight lines denoting water. A large winged insect is placed at the top center of the design.

Belgium, marked as above, M.V., c. 1860.

INDIAN TREE

Made by Grimwades Brothers

The outer edge of this plate is printed in a very dark blue. This is succeeded by a row of diamonds then a narrow light band. At five points a "V" shaped printing separates the rim, and five large sprawling stylized oriental type peonies are placed in the sections so provided. Angular stems from heavy prunus branches are placed beneath the large forms and form a wide wreath inside the well.

English, marked as above, Mk. 1823, L.V., c. 1891.

JAPAN

Made by Thomas Rathbone & Company

The sauce tureen photographed is decorated with a border band of brocade pattern consisting of stylized lotus forms separated by reserves of diamond diapering. Horizontal sprays of peony blossoms, buds and leaves are placed on the side of the body and are contained at the bottom by a narrow brocade band. The lid is decorated by two rows of single blossoms divided by the same narrow brocade.

English, marked T. R. & Co., Mk. 3205, Registry #545204, L.V., c. 1909.

LINCOLN

Made by Ashworth Brothers

The gravy boat pictured is printed in a greyish blue. The pattern consists of a wide band of realistic chrysanthemums with shaggy leaves. The top of the band is detailed with a narrow ribbon of scrolls and the bottom by a narrow geometric design of bars and "V" shapes.

English, marked as above, Mk. 141, L.V., c. 1890.

LOVELY LADY DRIVER

Maker Unknown

The rim of this portrait plate is embossed to form scallop reserves. The edge is covered with cobalt that fades towards the center. Gold tracery is placed over the reserves.

The young woman at the wheel of a car in the center is attired in a driving costume of pale blue trimmed with red.

This plate looks like the work of the French China Co. or the Sterling Potteries.

American, L.V.

LUCERNE

Made by New Wharf Pottery

This pattern is printed in a slate blue on a scalloped gilt edged saucer. The outer edge is trimmed with a band of bell flowers edged with tiny beads. Four Art Nouveau type vertical designs formed from foliated scrolls and terminating in a fleur-de-lis are linked together by garlands of realistic small flowers and sprigs.

English, marked as above, Mk. 2886, L.V., c. 1891.

MARQUIS II

Made by W. H. Grindley

This scalloped plate bears the same back marking and the same registry number as the Marquis pattern catalogued in "Flow Blue China An Aid to Identification", but the rim pattern is very different and consists of a circle of beads containing a small flower. Gold is used to outline the edge and is placed around the beads. The rim design ends in small scallops under the beads and a row of fleur-de-lis gives a spearpoint effect around the top of the well. There is no center medallion on these plates.

English, marked as above, Mk. 1843, the plate is dated May 9, 1906, L.V., c. 1906.

PANAMA CANAL

Made by Sterling China Co.

This plate, like the Calendar Plate #II shown in this book was made to commemorate the building of the Panama Canal. The rim of the dish is fluted and its edge is covered with cobalt that flows toward the center. The plate is entitled on its face "Old Glory" at the top of a map of the Panama Canal area. The map is encircled by medallions containing the pictures of the Presidents of the United States, up to and including William Howard Taft, (1909-1913), who as Secretary of War to T. R. Roosevelt had overseen the construction of the Canal and who had established the American Government in the Canal Zone.

American, marked as above, L.V., c. 1910.

PEKIN

Made by Samuel Keeling & Company

A cup plate is photographed and the central motif may not be typical of larger plates as it is composed of bell flowers on a heavy stem. However, the border probably remains the same on all pieces and consists of a triple section of fence separated by a coiled sprig of bell flowers and overscaled stylized oval buds flanked by six large leaves.

English, marked S. K. & Co., Mk. 2447, E.V., c. 1845.

PENANG

Made by Samuel Ford & Company

Six keyhole designs flanked by carnations and placed in an urn shape are separated by straight vertical bars that are topped by small hearts in this pattern. The design covers most of the plate and leaves only the center of the well open. The plate is unevenly scalloped and is embossed with scrolls.

English, marked as above, mark not located, L.V., c. 1905.

PERSIAN SPRAY

Made by Doulton & Company

The design on this scalloped plate appears to be more Oriental than Persian. Inset on a very dark cobalt border which is covered with gold tracery are six circular medallions of various sizes. Four contain a scene from the willow story and three contain a stylized flower set in snail-like scrolls. The floral design is repeated in both gold and blue in the center and five sprays of small flowers radiate from the three medallions grouped in the center of the plate.

English, marked as above, Mk. 1329, L.V., c. 1885,

RICHMOND

Made by Ford & Son

This pattern is printed in a very dark slate blue. The rim pattern consists of eight triangular designs of lilies flanked at the top by leaves. These are separated by horizontal bars at the bottom and quatrefoils at the top. Under the bars a sprig pendant design enters the well. The center medallion is composed of a field of scrolls and sprigs that surround a white circle.

English, marked F. & S., Mk. 1585, L.V., c. 1891.

RIDGWAY JAPAN

Made by Ridgways

The scalloped edge of this vegetable serving dish is enhanced by the typical gadroon embossed border featured by Ridgways. The rim design consists of stylized lotus blossoms flanked by dark foliated scrolls. Small flowers join the main designs and form a continuous wreath around the rim. The well is encircled by a band of oriental brocade consisting of oval floral reserves linked by diamonds containing quartrefoils. The basic blue pattern is over coloured with henna red in the floral parts of the pattern.

English, marked as above, Mk. 3313, L.V., c. 1910.

SHELL AND FLOWER

Made by Podmore Walker & Co.

The title on the backstamp of this plate is illegible so this name will be used to present the pattern.

The design appears on the dark edged rim and consists of three large shells framed within foliated cartouches. In the arches formed between the scrolls there are large dahlias and leaves and parts of these enter the well.

English, marked Wedgwood & Co. (imp.) and the early English coat of arms and "Paris White Ironstone", Mk. 3079, E.V., c. 1855.

SPRIGS

Made by Charles Meigh

The object photographed is a syrup jug. It is printed in a greyish blue in an allover design of berries and sprigs.

There is no name on the backstamp. This name is given to catalogue.

English, marked as above, and also marked with Meigh's Chinese mark, Mks. 2617 and 2618, E.V., c. 1851.

SPRINGTIME

Probably made by Brown,
Westhead, Moore & Co.

This plate bears no backstamp and this title is used to catalogue the pattern. The border design consists of strawberries, peaches, poppies, forget-me-nots, daisies, wild roses, lilies of the valley and bell flowers sprayed across a bamboo angular trellis design and large leafy scrolls. This printing is in slate blue. The center design in the matching color consists of lilacs and columbine. The outer scalloped embossed edge is decorated in dark cobalt.

English, marked (imp.) Cauldon, probably Mk. 681, Registry #184291, L.V., c. 1900.

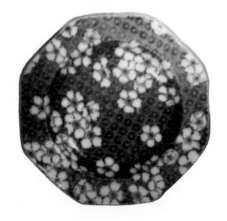

VOLANTE

Made by Brown, Westhead, Moore & Co.

This design consists of an overall pattern of prunus printed in a greyish blue. The diaper background consists of small hexagons with sunbursts in each one.

English, dated 1882, Mk. 679, L.V., c. 1882.

WENTWORTH

Made by J. & G. Meakin

The pattern on this scalloped plate is asymetrical. One large fernlike scroll edged with wheat, sprigs and flowers is balanced by two smaller scrolls of the same nature. The edge is embossed and gold has been used to highlight the embossing.

English, marked as above, Mk. 2602, L.V., c. 1907.

YORK

Made by Brown, Westhead, Moore & Co.

A paisley type design covers the face of the plate photographed. The outer edge is unevenly scalloped and is embossed with heavy scrolls that are covered with gold. Small morning glories and sprigs appear on the rim between the tops of the long foliated scrolls and sprays that enter the center of the well.

There is no name on the backstamp. The donor of the photograph thought the name might be "York". The name of Baroque is given in order to catalogue the pattern.

English, marked "Cauldon", Registry #199522, Mk. 681, L.V., c. 1893.

ZUYDER

Made by J. & G. Meakin

The jug photographed is decorated with fernlike scrolls that form a crescent slanted towards a design of sprigs of little flowers and scrolls at the left. The main design is flanked by Art Nouveau vertical stylized floral forms. The collar and base of the body and handle are all embossed and the details of these are gilded.

English, marked as above, Mk. 2602, L.V., c. 1907.

CORRECTIONS AND ADDENDA TO BOOK ONE

page 20   "CHUSAN". *Made by Joseph Clementson should be dated c. 1840. Clementson potted from 1839 to 1864 but did not use the Phoenix Bird mark which appears on this plate until after 1840. The date of 1830 given in the book is an error.*

page 78   "TYROLEAN". *This plate is backstamped "England" and should be dated after 1891. The number 3308 mark is incorrect. The correct mark number is 3303a which was first used from 1844-54. The mark was used at later periods by Ridgways.*

page 85   " ANEMONE " *has been proven to be made by Minton. B. B. meant "Best Body", English, L.V., c. 1890.*   (top)

page 124   "PANSY". *Has been identified as Lonsdale made by Samuel Ford & Co., English, Mk. 1604., L.V., c. 1910.*

page 135   "CAMPION". *See corrections for Book II.*

page 139   "TURIN"

page 147   "DUDLEY". *(Ford) This pattern was also made in cobalt.*

page 175   "DELPH". *The same pattern appears as "Delft" made by Mintons, English, Mk. 2706-2707, M.V., c. 1871,*

page 34   **"CHANG"**. *This is the same pattern as Ning Po made by Ralph Hall & Co. in 1845.*

page 65   **"WILLOW"**. *The pottery that made this pattern has been identified as Ashworth Bros. English, L.V., c. 1865, Mk. 146.*

page 67   **"YELLOW RIVER"**. *This pattern closely resembles the island pattern as seen on Canton and Nanking ware which pictured a river scene. (See Mudge's Chinese Export Porcelain, page 140).*

page 68   **"SINGAN"**. *Made by Thomas Goodfellow. The plate at lower left is fourteen-sided and is panelled. The rim of the mold has inverted scallops at the well. The outer edge of the plate is decorated with a narrow band of diamond diapering interrupted by small oval floral reserves. This design is repeated around the well.*

The rim design consists of sprays of stylized over-scaled flowers which alternate with small scenes of a pagoda set on a rock. A willow tree is at the left and a palm tree is at right.

The central scene is dominated by a tall wide willow tree that grows from an island at the left and whose branches cross over the center of the well. A small garden house is at the left of the tree. A large pagoda is placed on a rocky island under the tree branches at the center of the picture. An angled bridge connects the islands and two men are fishing from it. There are five smaller islands placed around the main design, one at the left has a small willow tree and one at the top has a double-roof pagoda.

Singan at first glance is almost identical to Manilla by Podmore Walker and is often confused with it. But the flowers on the rim are different (stylized peonies on Manilla and two different blossoms on Singan). The rim scenes differ in that on Manilla a small willow tree is placed at the left and an apple tree is at the right of the pagoda. The central scenes on Manilla, the photograph of which is shown at lower right, depicts a large tree rising from the right of the pattern, the bridge is a rounded arch form, and the two men are carrying a lantern. The background islands differ in that the placing of the largest which bears the pagoda is at top left.

English, marked as above, and "Ironstone", Mk. 1738, E.V., c. 1845.

page 69   **"CHUSAN".** *(page 20, Book I). Some correspondents have written that this pattern is marked P. H. & Co. or R. H. & Co. Robert Hall, Swanbank Potteries, 1841-45, became Podmore, Walker in 1853. Perhaps between 1849 and 1853, the Company was Podmore Hall & Co. The only P. H. & Co. listed in any available reference is for Peter Holdcroft & Co. of Burslem, who potted 1846-52 and it is possible that this is his work. but the impressed rosette distinctly indicates the Podmore, Walker firm.*

page 84   **"BIRDS AT FOUNTAIN".** *The correct name of the pattern has been found and the maker identified. This is "INDIA" by Villeroy & Boch. German, marked with said name, and V. & B. See Thorn, Mk. 43, page 37, L.V., c. 1880.*

page 106   **"SYRIA".** *The maker of this pattern has been ascertained to be Robert Cochran of Scotland. Scottish, marked R. C. & Co., Mk. 965, c. 1846.*

page 107   **"TOWER".** *A soup bowl has been found in Canada with the mark R. M. & Co. on the back stamp. This could be Rowland & Marcellus Co., English, L.V., c. 1905.*

page 109   **"VENETIAN SCENERY".** *Another bowl in this pattern was observed at an antique show and it was printed in dark cobalt and was definitely flown.*

page 126   **"BROOKLYN".** *This pattern was also made with colors of brown, orange and gold placed over the blue underprint.*

page 132   **"DERBY".** *This pattern was also produced in dark blue without the henna red.*

page 155   **"RINCEAUX".** *Dates L.V., c. 1880.*

page 169   **"JARDINIERE".** *This pattern is not the Dresden by V. & B. It is very much like Bouquet by Nowotny, page 126, Book II. However it differs in that it has a bouquet in the center. The maker's name should read V. & B. However this may also be true of the large plates made by Nowotny.*

page 173   **"ACANTHA".** *Was also made with cobalt blue printing.*

page 175   **"CAMPION".**

page 184 **"BALTIC"**. *The Registry number is 43308.*

page 198 **"TOKIO"**.

page 215 **"ASTER AND GRAPESHOT"**. *An example has been found marked "Clementson", "Shelton". English, made by Joseph Clementson, Mk. 910B, E.V. c. 1840.*

page 222 **"LUSTRE BAND"**. *Examples have been found marked with the pattern name Tulip.*

page 223 **"PEACH BLOSSOM"**. *Examples have been found marked C. Collinson & Co., English, made by Charles Collinson & Co., Mk. 1013, N.V., c. 1860.*

page 226 **"STICK SPATTER"**. *This pattern is known in Pennsylvania as "Snow Flake Stick Spatter".*

page 236 **"AURORA"**. *The maker has been identified as Francis Morley, English, Mk. 2761, E.V., c. 1850.*

page 240 **"COCKATOO"**. *The correct name of the pattern has been found and the maker identified. This is "INDIA" by Villeroy & Boch. German, marked with said name, and V. & B. See Thorn, Mk. 43, page 37, L.V., c. 1880.*

page 242 **"CRAWFORD RANGES"**. *This pattern has turned up in the shape of a small syrup pitcher with the mark of the Upper Hanley Pottery Co. on the back stamp.*

page 269 **SYRIAN"**. *Reportedly was also printed in dark cobalt blue.*

page 280 *The deep dish is labeled Lahore in a Cartouche. Maker ~~un~~known.*

DELHI BY BLACKHURST & TUNNICLIFFE. AUTHOR'S COLLECTION.
(ACTUAL SIZE)

NOTES ON

MINIATURE DISHES

MADE IN FLOW BLUE AND MULBERRY PATTERNS

Children's toy dishes and miniature dishes made for gifts, or as samples, have always been popular, and collectors exist who vie avidly for them. This was also true in times past. The skill and artistry necessary to make a small replica both beautiful and functional has always excited admiration. The price structure has never changed in relation to the prices of ordinary adult china ware, and remains high today, because relatively few small dishes were produced. It is possible that some were made as salesmen's samples, or perhaps for exhibitions, but most were probably made for children's use and pleasure. In the Flow Blue field there are a few patterns that seem to have been made exclusively for children: "Basket", "Forget-Me-Not", and "Delhi" for example. Famous patterns, including Scinde, Amoy and Pelew were also applied to miniature dishes and these are in great demand today.

Remember that tea sets did not include dinner plates or serving dishes. Dinner sets of the early Victorian days did not include cups and saucers or tea pots or sugarbowls or creamers, waste bowls or pie (dessert) plates. As you can see in the large photograph of the dinner set in "Forget-Me-Not", the set is almost complete with platters, covered dishes and sauce tureens. The ladle in the foreground is 3½" long. There are no cups and saucers because these would have to be bought separately in a tea set.

As we have noted, scarcity is the factor that causes high prices when demand is great. The older the pattern, the longer time of usage, the fewer are the examples which survive. It appears from the date of the patterns used that most miniature dishes in Flow Blue and Mulberry were made before 1860. The conclusion must be that they are a very scarce item in a popular and not too plentiful collecting field.

**MINIATURE MULBERRY TEA
SERVICE, PELEW PATTERN**

**MINIATURE FLOW BLUE TEA CUPS AND
SAUCERS, BASKET PATTERN**

**MINIATURE FLOW BLUE TEA SERVICES
AMOY PATTERN**

**MINIATURE FLOW BLUE DINNER SET. FOR-GET-ME-NOT PATTERN.
PHOTOGRAPHS COURTESY BEVERLY LABE**

**MINIATURE FLOW BLUE
TEA SET EXAMPLES**

**STANDARD AND MINIATURE
SCINDE SOUP TOUREENS**

PHOTOGRAPHS COURTESY OF LOIS TUCKER

PRICING PROCEDURES

I

BUYING FLOW BLUE CHINA FOR PLEASURE AND INVESTMENT

This section of Book III is written for the benefit of collectors of Flow Blue China and for those persons who are interested in the related field of Mulberry Ware. It is intended as a sort of Primer to introduce the amateur collector to the way values are arrived at so that he can buy and sell with some confidence. Value can be defined as estimated worth. Worth can be defined as the quality of a thing which renders it important. Therefore, the term is relevant. This is especially true in our field. A certain old stoneware pattern may be very much desired by Mr. Smith who places great importance upon acquiring an example of it, but Mrs. Jones may harbor an equal longing for a late Victorian pitcher and basin. Neither would strive to obtain the other's object and might find it difficult to understand such a search and the resultant expenditure.

It is true today that many sellers in shops and shows place a high price on any piece of Flow Blue they display, regardless of whether the pattern has merit and is collectible, or is very late, in poor condition, or just a curiosity. Confusion exists in this field because many prospective purchasers and expectant sellers do not understand the different categories that this pottery must be divided into in order to establish values.

A great deal of Flow Blue China qualifies as antique as it is well over 100 years old, which is the criterion set up by usage and custom. Much is of heirloom quality, dating after 1875 and up to the turn of the century and into the early years of the 20th century. The McKinley Act which forced foreign manufacturers to mark their wares permanently took effect in 1891. Fifteen years after our bicentennial celebration in 1976, the McKinley Act will have been in force over a century and almost all of the old Flow Blue extant will become officially antique.

A word of warning is necessary here. Simply because an object is 100 years old does not enhance its original beauty, workmanship or utility. The halo of old age is apt to give an aura to objects and we are inclined to venerate any article on the basis of age alone. But look around you at the rocks and stones; they are not more or less beautiful than they were at the day of their Creation, smaller perhaps from attrition, but in reality little different. Age cannot be the sole factor in arriving at value, but it is extremely important in our field of study.

Old age today carries no cachet or honor when it applies to the "senior citizens" of our country. But the nostalgic trend, now current among young persons who are seeking "old" items from the jazz age of the Twenties, song sheets from the sad depression days of the Thirties, and even enemy mementos from our war against Hitler, points up a peculiar truth about trash and treasure. Today's children show little love or respect for older people, which is a phenomenon new to civilization. They also show little interest in their parents' values or life style, and by extension, to their parents' possessions, but this is not exactly new. The young always have to skip back a few generations to find interesting and worthwhile treasure to acquire. The latter does not apply just to today; it has happened over and over again before our time. The parents' mundane belongings are often spurned as being of little value. How true this is of everyday dishes. Think how indifference and carelessness took a toll of the vast amounts of inexpensive Flow Blue China that was exported from England to this country from 1840 onward.

Therefore, we must start to classify for value by first determining age, not with the idea that age is good, but with the knowledge that old Flow Blue is scarce. This refers especially to the early stoneware and ironstone patterns from 1840 to 1860-70. Any piece of the early patterns should be considered desirable as long as it is in good to fine condition.

A word here about mended pieces and those that have small flaws that do not detract from the attractiveness of the pattern. If you want examples of a pattern or a mold and find them in a flawed piece, it is my belief, and that of all the dealers whom I respect, that you should go ahead and buy contingent upon a lesser price for the item. There are collectors who are purists who seek to purchase mint perfect pieces. This is fine if they have the means to satisfy their own demand for perfection. However most dealers shy away from the word "mint" as this implies a state equal to the newness of an item just passed by the inspector at the factory. China used over 100 years has knife marks in the glaze surface on the face, and the glaze on the foot rim may be worn away. Flow Blue China was not put up in a special cabinet such as that which a Ming vase might require, nor was it kept untouched for generations except for an occasional careful cleaning. This china in which we are interested saw much everyday service. In my opinion this fact adds to its interest and attests its durability.

Some patterns, in both the early and later Victorian eras were made in profusion, others appear as oddities. It would seem logical to assume that this happened because some designs were instantly popular and in great demand. The potters therefore made huge quantities in order to meet the demand. Evidently the popularity remained constant through the time span from manufacture until today. Such names as Amoy, Scinde, Temple, Pelew and Chapoo from the early stage, Touraine, Holland Argyle (Grindley) and Waldorf from the later era are still very popular, and in great demand. The supply continues fairly large. This list is not to be construed as conferring value only on the patterns named. However, those commanding the higher prices are those that are best known, and most wanted for that reason. The lesser known patterns are just as desirable as far as workmanship and beauty, and can be obtained at lower prices.

In making up the price lists, it has been dificult to place even an approximate value on many designs. After years of cataloging patterns, my experience has proved that some are oddities and not parts of dinner or tea sets, some are borderline and not really Flow Blue *per se*, some would appear experimental in nature, especially in the use of blue dyes. The only reasonable way for a purchaser to figure out a fair price for these odd designs, is to evaluate the age, beauty of pattern, fineness of execution, the potter (if a back stamp exists), and to come to a subjective judgment on what the price should be. This applies equally to dealers and collectors. Since "Flow Blue China, An Aid to Identification", appeared in 1971, and Flow Blue became a commodity in antique shows, it has been appalling to this writer to see an odd plate with perhaps a late, skimpy slate blue, *art nouveau* — floral design mixture on the rim only, marked with a price as high as a plate of old stoneware would command. It is up to the purchaser to be discriminating. If the dealer is ignorant or greedy, the purchaser must use her own knowledge and be careful. Just because a dish has some Flow Blue factor does not automatically make it a gem of great worth. Be careful. Be selective. If it is cheap and amuses you, then why not add it to your collection for contrast? If it is expensive and you are aware that it is not worth the price for any reason, why think twice about it? The best warning cannot be repeated too often, go to an honest dealer. There was an oval wash basin offered at a flea market in Louisville; it dated around 1900, the design was nondescript; the maker was unknown and the price (without a pitcher) was $200! In the writer's possession there is an ad from a very respectable trade source offering a Flow Blue plate for $500! There are always get-rich-quick-people in business. When prices are not censured or controlled in any way, sellers who possess little or no knowledge of their wares try to make a big profit. Dishonest sellers who do have knowledge do the same thing. This ignorance and greed can be grievously expensive for the purchaser.

There are patterns being made today in this country and in England. They resemble old and famous patterns but they are not really duplicates. One even states on the bottom that it is Flow Blue. Can you imagine Davenport or Grindley marking their wares that way? They knew what they were producing, so did their buyers. Flow Blue is a colouring process, the equivalent marking would be to put on the bottom of a plastic plate of emerald hue "Green". Ridiculous, but many have purchased the new wares on the market and thought they were old. The manufacturers are not making false claims; they are making new Flow Blue, because when an item becomes popular and saleable someone always wants to jump on the band wagon and go for the ride. The motive is profit, and this is not un-American. Buy the new if you like it, but study enough about the old Flow Blue that you will not mistake the new for the old.

The best way to buy Flow Blue China is to know the dates of manufacture, know the potteries and their marks, know the patterns and all about the particular ones in which you are interested. Above all, before you spend good money, make certain that you fully realize the worth of what you are purchasing. If you have doubts about value or authenticity, the only safe way to purchase is through a reputable dealer. If you really apply yourself to understanding this limited field, you can sally forth and search for blue treasure with confidence.

P.S. All above applies to Mulberry Ware, also.

PRICING PROCEDURES

II

SELLING FLOW BLUE CHINA

It is usually a lot easier to buy something you want than it is to sell anything you are forced to put a price on and then merchandise. At present, however, this statement does not apply to collectors or possessors of Flow Blue China who have decided to sell their pieces of this ware. There are many prospective purchasers for most of the patterns and the only difficulty that the seller will meet is how to find other collectors or dealers and how to price. Price does not always reflect value, of course; sometimes other factors intervene. But if you understand how most antique dealers arrive at their prices you may be better able to assess the market. The average collector is mystified and confused about the various prices asked for similar goods by different dealers. Let us examine why this apparent contradiction exists. Most Flow Blue dealers try to obtain a mark-up of from 25 per cent to 33⅓ per cent. If a plate costs $12 it is marked to sell at $15 or $16. If a rival dealer has bought at $10, the plate will be marked about $13.50. This low mark-up is found in fields where goods are in short supply and the demand is great.

Because the field of Flow Blue China has been documented, there are very few bargains left. Many clients who visit a dealer's shop will quote a price they noted several years ago of a platter for a "dollar", or a mint Scinde tureen for "$25". As I related in my first book, Flow Blue China was not always cherished any more than some plastic dishes are today. To someone who considered the dishes close to trash, anyone paying real dollars for them was deemed foolish and the price paid was "found money" as far as the shrewd seller was concerned. But there have been collectors who loved the blue patterns and preserved their dishes with care. Such a collection as that of Mrs. Woodrow Wilson, shown in "Flow Blue China II" is testimony to this fact.

The dealers are in somewhat the same position as the collectors. They cannot obtain Flow Blue China today at the prices that prevailed a few years ago. Just 10 years ago it was not in demand and those dealers who stocked it did not pay much and therefore could sell it at a fair and low price, and still make a good profit. Today, because of the interest, knowledge, and demand of collectors, Flow Blue is becoming a difficult item for a dealer to stock and as a result even with a modest mark-up for each dealer who handles the articles the price has spiraled upwards. This is not the fault of the dealers, it is a result of the demand upon the supply. The dealer must eat and is entitled to a profit, although many customers seem to resent and resist this fact. Many shoppers, who would not stoop to bargain at a dress shop, department store or candy counter, or with a doctor or lawyer, because they realize everyone in business is working for his daily bread, seem to have the attitude that they expect to be cheated by antique dealers and must bargain and threaten the loss of a sale in order to protect themselves. Reputable antique dealers should not be treated like charlatans. Get to know your dealer and trust him. He is bearing the burden of securing saleable merchandise, displaying it and pricing it according to supply and demand. Knowledgeable dealers do know the market and they price accordingly. They buy good popular items and sell as quickly as possible at a small profit. That is why you will not meet many wealthy antique dealers. Of course, there are the exceptions who buy and sell large volumes of precious goods for a wealthy clientele, but for the most part the average, honest, small dealer makes a modest living albeit he leads an independent, interesting and busy life.

But, you say, that is all about dealers. How about a collector who wants to sell or is forced by circumstances to dispose of his Flow Blue? Let me say this, you have many choices.

First, you can sell on consignment to a dealer whom you know and trust. After you have agreed upon the price you want to be paid, he will display your goods and try to sell them for you. If you have agreed to take $200 and he gets $250 he keeps the $50 as compensation for time, exhibition and sales effort. If you sell this way, be sure to get an agreement in writing that sets forth the receipt of the itemized pieces you are selling and the price and the terms agreed upon; be sure that you and the consignee each get a copy and that both are dated and signed by both parties.

Second, you can approach a dealer in person or by mail. It is up to you to do this with a dealer you know personally or know by his good reputation. It is usually futile to ask an established dealer what he will pay you for a particular thing. You should have a good idea of what you want and be able to state your price. If you do not, and the dealer offers you a small amount, you might consider that you are being cheated. On the other hand, the dealer has to purchase with the idea of resale, and it is natural that he is seeking a bargain. If your price is too high it is unrealistic to expect a dealer to purchase. But remember that a reputable dealer who runs a successful business, has the cash to purchase your wares, and probably will not barter with you. If the price is right he will buy. If your price is too high for him to make a turn over, he will tell you so and may offer you less. He will not try to cheat you, but he must buy at a price that he can raise for resale.

Third, you can approach other collectors whom you may know. Often it happens that such a person has expressed an interest in your Flow Blue. You can contact this prospect by letter, or call, and state that you are going to dispose of part of your holdings. You do not have to give a reason for this; everyone weeds out their goods as they change and grow older.

Fourth, you can advertise your pieces of Flow Blue in the newspaper in its classified advertising department under the "Antiques" caption, or, if your paper has such, under "Special Sales". All you have to do is say "Flow Blue for Sale," and give your phone number. You will be deluged with calls. But if you are timid or do not want to deal with strangers this is not for you.

Fifth, you can advertise in the papers and magazines that collectors and dealers in Antiques read. Go to your library and ask about these. In writing your ads for this medium, you must specify just what you are selling: Pattern, maker, what particular piece (plate? how large?), and usually price. Blind ads without prices given are suspect and you will not get many replies. Headline your ad "FLOW BLUE" and you will be surprised at the replies. Of course, you must be prepared to pack very carefully and ship and insure whatever you sell.

By the way, if you want to sell a set of China, state the number of pieces in your set. When a dealer says a set of dishes has a certain number of pieces in it, he is counting every piece. That means sugar bowl lids, and gravy trays and tureen tops and cups and saucers. A butter dish with drainer and lid is three pieces in the trade. Also if you advertise a set of dishes, remember that to a dealer a set of dishes usually means how many cups and saucers are in it. A set is judged by the number of complete table settings which usually include cups and saucers. The only exception to this is old stoneware, because there the cups and saucers were sold as part of a separate tea set.

If a dealer answers your ad, he may suggest a lot price, by which he means he will purchase all the items you advertised, but likely at a price less than you had hoped. If you are one of the smart set who purchased at a very low price, you may very well be able to accept less money in order to sell quickly and, with luck, to dispose of the entire lot which does away with a lot of shipping and fuss. But if his offer does not suit you, at least understand his position and refuse his offer with grace.

Now, of course, the question is, "How do I set a price on my Flow Blue"?

You arrive at a sales price by determining what you paid for an item. If you inherited it or bought it for a ridiculously low price as a lucky bargain, you will have to figure out the present value in relationship to what you wish to achieve. If your cost was little or nothing, only you can judge the price. If you have little interest in the field, ask a reasonable price, or offer a bargain, make a fast sale and invest in something that you feel is worthwhile and rewarding. If you purchased the article recently you have some idea of current worth. If you have been collecting for years and are forced by circumstances, or a loss of interest, to sell, you must take into consideration the money you have spent, the years involved, and the present value of your holding. If you were methodical you probably kept an inventory record as you purchased finds for your collection, so you can use that as a basis.

You can get an idea of value from price lists such as those in this book, but remember that guides to prices are just guides. Values depend upon scarcity, the beauty of execution and the popularity of certain patterns in certain geographic locations, Gaudy Dutch in Pennsylvania, for example. You know your own area and can use that knowledge to sell there. If you are going to sell, use a formula based on what you paid, the age of the pattern, the condition of the ware, and the general popularity of the pattern as you understand it. Consult the value guides in this book, but remember all the above factors can affect your sale. There are buyers for your Flow Blue, just don't price yourself too high and out of the market.

PRICING PROCEDURES

III

UNDERSTANDING THE FLOW BLUE PRICE GUIDES

Values are arrived at by using a combination of contributing factors. Dealers who specialize in the field set prices based on the purchase price they paid for an item plus their profit. Years of experience educate such a dealer as to what patterns are in the most demand among his clientele and he will purchase specific patterns for certain customers. What the dealer pays almost always dictates the selling price. If a lot of clients want the same pattern the basic price goes higher as the availability of the china diminishes.

Geography plays a large part in pricing at present. The prices of Flow Blue and Mulberry are generally lower in the Northeast and Midwest than in the rest of the country, as there is more available stock there. Prices are generally higher in the Far West, the Southwest and in the South, with the exception of the Atlantic Seaboard. Of course, these price differences will tend to decrease as Flow Blue becomes nationally known and desired by collectors.

Pattern acceptance determines values also. The eminence of the pattern, the condition and depth of colour and clarity of pattern must all be considered. In Flow Blue collecting there are two schools on this subject alone. Some collectors want the most deeply blurred cobalt examples they can find and others prefer to discern the romantic and exotic patterns.

The mold shape is also a factor in setting value. There are a lot of saucers extant that have lost their cups. There are more nine inch plates than ten inch ones, because the larger plates were used three times a day and more often broken. Tea pots, sugar bowls, all lids, and pitchers were subject to heavy use and many were destroyed, or thrown away when slightly damaged. Pitchers are scarce for another reason. For many years there have been collectors who buy only pitchers, of any and every sort, and this included Flow Blue.

When you use the value guides keep in mind that these are current prices for fine examples of Flow Blue China. Price depends upon the availability of an object, the value set upon it by the seller and the ability and readiness of a prospective purchaser to buy. The prices quoted are guideposts to help you ascertain value, whether you are buying or selling. They are not rigid figures, but are based upon scarcity, age, collectors' acceptance and excellence of design and workmanship.

If an article does not meet the standard of perfection as required by the lists, the fair price should be much lower, perhaps by one-third to one-half. A word here about mended wares done professionally; if the piece is rare and useful or beautifully restored without excessive mending, its value is not impaired to the extent that the price would be very much below the value indicated, but it still would not command the average price given.

As to appraisals and appraisers. A collector who has a sizeable amount of Flow Blue China and who realizes that values have advanced very rapidly, may want to insure his possessions. The figures herein can be used in appraisal, but, remember, an accredited appraiser will want to see the wares and determine whether they are of fine condition or not and set a value accordingly. It is most important to identify correctly a pattern when reference is made to a price guide. In our field many patterns bear identical names and errors could come about in valuing a piece of Flow Blue. If you do get an appraisal be certain to employ a reputable person, who is qualified to appraise and who can show you his credentials. His appraisal will be in writing and he will sign and date it. It is wise to get a couple of copies, for yourself and for your insurance company. The appraiser will expect a fee and will discuss this with you before starting. The cost of replacement because of theft, fire or disaster depends upon the market place at the time of the loss. The market price keeps rising, therefore, you should not neglect having your collection re-evaluated as the years go by.

The value lists that I have compiled are a code for collectors to understand and use. The letter A means that the pattern is old, early Victorian. If there is a plus sign after the A, the + symbol means that the pattern is valued near the top price given for the article.

For example, if you wish to learn the current value for an Amoy teapot, you would refer to the pattern Index. Amoy is listed as A+. You then refer to the A list of early Victorian patterns and look for the prices quoted for teapots. The plus sign tells you that the value, if the teapot is in fine condition, is in the uppermost range of the values quoted.

If your pattern is coded A without a plus or minus sign, the letter means that the design is early Victorian, and the value is within the range as quoted.

If the design is coded A−, the letter and symbol signify that the pattern is old, but not well known, and is not currently popular. It does not command as high a price as those quoted on the list. This must not be construed as denigrating the pattern or the potter; many fine designs exist, perhaps not yet even catalogued, that are not in current demand because of colour or design.

The other symbols given in the Index, B+, B, and B—, etc. are to be construed in the same manner. The letter B signifies a late Victorian pattern, and B+ means that the pattern is very popular and at this time commands a high price. B means the average value as given in the B price list, and B— would be a value below those presented.

The C list relates to late Victorian miscellany. If you wish to evaluate a jardiniere for example, look at list C for the value range.

The D list refers to Art Nouveau and the plus or minus signs apply here also.

The E list covers Victorian specialty items such as souvenir plates, and the X list is explained on the price list heading.

"Oh, for the prices of yesterday!"

P. Williams

"But where are the snows of yesteryear?"

F. Villon

FLOW BLUE
Value List A

Values for Early Victorian patterns (1840-1875) in excellent condition.

WARNING: These figures are a value GUIDE. They are not rigid market prices. It is impossible to formulate a guide that encompasses all conditions. Prices are subject to constant change. These figures are current (1975) in most areas of the United States.

STONEWARE DINNER SERVICE

1. PLATES

Plate 10 to 10½"	$42.00–$55.00
Plate 9 to 9½"	$27.50–$40.00
Plate 8"+	$27.00–$35.00
Plate 7"+	$20.00–$27.50

2. DEEP DISHES

Deep dish (soup) with flange 10 to 10½"	$35.00–$50.00
Deep dish (soup) with flange 9 to 9½"	$27.50–$40.00
Dish with flange (cereal, pudding or ice cream) 7 to 8"	$30.00+
Sauce dish 5 to 5¾"	$20.00–$30.00

3. PLATTERS

Platter, well and tree	$350.00
Fish drainer for same	$150.00+
Platter 22 to 24"	$250.00
Platter 20"	$225.00
Platter 16 to 18"	$150.00–$200.00
Platter 12 to 14"	$90.00–$125.00
Platter (egg) 10"	$75.00
Meat charger (round platter) 12"+	$125.00–$150.00+

4. VEGETABLE SERVING PIECES

(These 4 form a nest)

Flat round "potato" bowl
(in N. England "Bean Bowl") 14" . . . . $75.00–$95.00

Flat round vegetable bowl 12" . . . . $65.00–$80.00

Flat round vegetable bowl 10" . . . . $60.00–$75.00

Flat round vegetable bowl 8" . . . . $55.00–$70.00

Nest complete $300.00

Octagonal vegetable bowls (open) . . . . $65.00–$90.00

Octagonal vegetable bowls (with lid) . . . .$150.00+

(These form a nest)

Oval octagonal vegetable servers 13½ to 14" long . . . $75.00+

Oval octagonal vegetable server 11½ to 12" long . . . . $65.00+

Oval octagonal vegetable server 9½ to 10" long . . . . $60.00+

Oval octagonal vegetable server 7½ to 8" long . . . . . $60.00+

Nest complete . . . .$300.00+

5. MISCELLANEOUS SERVING ITEMS FOUND IN DINNER SERVICES

Soup tureen with lid (Lid has hole for ladle) . . . .$450.00+

Stand (tray) for soup tureen . . . . $125.00–$150.00

Soup ladle . . . .$90.00–$125.00

(All three above matching) $725.00

Sauce tureen with lid (Lid has hole for ladle) . . .$95.00–$125.00

Stand (tray) for above . . . . $50.00–$60.00

Sauce ladle . . . .$75.00–$100.00

(All three above matching) . . . . $225.00–$300.00

Gravy boat (conventional shape) . . . . $65.00–$80.00

Stand for gravy boat . . . . $40.00–$50.00

(Two pieces matching) $145.00

Butter dish with drainer and lid $200.00

Mustard pot with lid $125.00

Drainer for butter dish $75.00

Shell shaped (or mitten) relish dish . . . .$85.00–$100.00

6. TEA SERVICE

Tea pot with lid	$250.00
Coffee pot with lid	$250.00
Creamer	$125.00
Sugar Bowl with lid	$100.00–$125.00
Waste Bowl	$65.00–$95.00
Milk pitcher (1 pint to 1½ pints)	$125.00–$135.00
Milk pitcher (1 quart)	$125.00–$150.00
Water pitcher (1½ quarts)	$150.00–$175.00
Water pitcher (2 quarts)	$150.00–$175.00
Tea bowl (handleless) with saucer	$50.00–$65.00
Coffee cup (handleless) with saucer	$50.00–$65.00
Coffee cup (mug type)	$65.00+
Handled cup with saucer	$50.00–$65.00
Cup plate 4 to 4½" diameter ½" deep	$30.00–$36.00
Toddy plate 5¼ to 5½" diameter	$40.00+
Honey dish 4" diameter ¾" deep	$40.00+

7. DESSERT SERVICE

Center piece (usually oblong and on pedestal base)	$125.00–$200.00
Stand for above	$100.00–$125.00
Cake plate with handles (open or not)	$90.00–$125.00
Oval serving dishes flat with handle on one end	$95.00+
Fruit bowl (plain)	$125.00+
Fruit bowl with reticulated sides	$300.00+
Stand (or tray) for fruit bowl	$200.00+
Compote (comport)	$125.00+
Individual service plate (pie plate) 6"	$30.00

8. AVAILABLE SERVING ITEMS FOUND IN OPEN STOCK

Syrup jug with lid	$75.00+
Punch bowl, Posset bowl, Syllabub bowl	$300+
Tyg	$150.00
Custard cups, Syllabub cups, Punch cups, Posset cups	$40.00+

(All look like child's cup with pedestal base – see illustration, this book)

9. CHAMBER SETS

Water pitcher (or ewer) . . . .$200.00+

Wash basin . . . . $150.00–$200.00

Set of pitcher and basin . . . .$400.00+

Hot water pitcher (1 to 1½ quarts) $125.00

Oblong flat tooth brush box . . . .$85.00–$125.00

Sponge dish with lid and drainer $125.00

Soap box with drainer and lid . . . .$85.00–$125.00

Mug . . . . $75.00+

Waste jar with drainer and lid $250.00

Chamber pot with lid . . . . $150.00–$200.00

(All above matching) . . . . $800.00–$1,000.00

FLOW BLUE
Value List B

Values for Late Victorian Patterns (1875–c. 1900) in fine condition.

WARNING: These figures are a value GUIDE. They are not rigid market prices. It is impossible to formulate a guide that encompasses all conditions. Prices are subject to constant change. These figures are current (1975) in most areas of the United States.

LATE VICTORIAN PATTERNS IN FINE CONDITION

Dinner plate 10"	$25.00–$30.00
Supper plate 9"	$17.00–$20.00
Luncheon plate 8"	$15.50–$17.00
Salad plate 7"	$10.00–$15.00
Pie plate 6"	$15.00–$20.00
Charger (Round platter) 14"	$100.00+
Well and Tree Platter	$100.00+
Platter 18"	$95.00
Platter 16"	$85.00
Platter 14"	$60.00–$75.00
Platter 12"	$35.00
Sauce dish	$12.50–$15.00
Soup dish (flat)	$17.50
Soup plate with flange	$20.00
Cereal bowl	$15.00
Individual oval vegetable dish 4"	$25.00
Butter pat	$9.00 –$15.00
Tea cup and saucer	$25.00–$40.00
Coffee cup and saucer	$30.00+
Bone dish	$15.00–$20.00
Chocolate cup/saucer	$35.00
Egg cup	$25.00–$30.00
Demi-tasse/saucer	$30.00+
Salad or berry bowl 10"	$45.00–$50.00
Oval vegetable bowl 12"	$40.00
Oval vegetable bowl 10"	$37.50

Oval vegetable bowl 9". $35.00
Covered butter dish with drainer. . . . . $85.00–$125.00
Gravy boat with stand . . . . $65.00–$85.00
Round vegetable dish with lid . . . . $65.00–$85.00
Covered oval vegetable dish . . . . $85.00–$125.00
Relish dish . . . . $45.00-$50.00
Soup tureen $200.00
Soup ladle $80.00
Stand for tureen $100.00
    All above matched $400.00
Tea pot $150.00
Creamer $65.00
Sugar with lid $65.00
Waste bowl . . . . $40.00–$50.00
Coffee pot $200.00
Milk pitcher 1 quart $95.00
Water pitcher 1½ quart $125.00

FLOW BLUE
Value List C

Values for Late Victorian, Miscellany in excellent condition.

WARNING: These figures are a value GUIDE. They are not rigid market prices. It is impossible to formulate a guide that encompasses all conditions. Prices are subject to constant change. These figures are current (1975) in most areas of the United States.

LATE VICTORIAN MISCELLANY

HOUSEHOLD ITEMS:

Clock	$150.00
Pedestal 20"	$125.00
Jardiniere	$60.00–$95.00
Biscuit Jar	$35.00–$50.00
Umbrella stand	$125.00+
Milk jugs (set of 3 graduated)	$150.00
Toilet bowl	$250.00+
Sink basin	$150.00+
Plant holder (depending on size)	$60.00–$100.00
Tea caddy	$45.00+
Foot bath	$200.00
Vase (depending on size) 4" to 14"	$35.00–$125.00

CHAMBER SETS:

Basin	$50.00+
Pitcher	$75.00–$100.00
Pitcher and basin (matched)	$175.00–$200.00
Toothbrush holder	$35.00+
Chamber pot with lid	$75.00+
Waste jar with lid	$100.00
Hot water pitcher	$75.00+
Mug	$45.00+
Sponge dish with drainer and lid	$50.00+
Soap dish with drainer and lid	$50.00+
Set all above matching	$600.00

DRESSER SETS:

Candlestick . . . . $50.00+

Hair Receiver . . . . $25.00+

Hairpin tray 3 x 5 . . . . $20.00–$35.00

Powder box with lid . . . . $30.00+

Tray 7 x 18 . . . . $50.00–$65.00

Hat pin holder . . . . $25.00–$35.00

FLOW BLUE
Value List D

Values for Art Nouveau patterns (c. 1900) in fine condition.

WARNING: These figures are a value GUIDE. They are not rigid market prices. It is impossible to formulate a guide that encompasses all conditions. Prices are subject to constant change. These figures are current (1975) in most areas of the United States.

ART NOUVEAU c. 1900

Dinner plate 10"	$15.00–$20.00
Supper plate 9"	$12.50–$17.00
Luncheon plate 8"	$12.50–$17.00
Salad plate 7"	$10.00–$15.00
Pie plate 6"	$10.00–$13.50
Platter 18"	$50.00–$60.00
Platter 16"	$40.00–$50.00
Platter 14"	$30.00–$40.00
Platter 12"	$20.00+
Sauce dish	$10.00+
Soup dish flat	$12.00+
Soup plate with flange	$12.50–$15.00
Cereal bowl	$10.00
Butter pat	$8.00–$12.00
Tea cup and saucer	$20.00–$25.00
Coffee cup and saucer	$20.00–$25.00
Berry bowl (salad bowl)	$22.00–$27.50
Oval vegetable 12"	$17.00–$25.00
Oval vegetable 10"	$15.00–$22.00
Gravy boat with stand	$50.00
Covered vegetable dish	$60.00+
Soup ladle	$60.00
Soup tureen	$150.00
Stand for above	$75.00
Sugar bowl with lid	$50.00+
Creamer	$50.00+
Milk pitcher	$50.00+
Tea pot	$95.00+

FLOW BLUE
Value List E

Values for Victorian Novelty Plates in fine condition.

WARNING: These figures are a value GUIDE. They are not rigid market prices. It is impossible to formulate a guide that encompasses all conditions. Prices are subject to constant change. These figures are current (1975) in most areas of the United States.

Souvenir Plates	$12.50–$25.00
Game Plates	$25.00+
Fish Plates	$20.00+
Animal Plates	$25.00+
Portrait Plates	$15.00–$35.00
Calendar Plates	$15.00
Premium Plates	$15.00–$25.00
Premium Pitchers	$45.00
Plaques (to be hung on wall as pictures)	$25.00+

FLOW BLUE
Value X

X Indicates patterns that are extraneous to the categories created for valuation purposes. The letter **"X"** used after a pattern in the Valuations Index applies to the patterns that were acquired primarily to photograph for the books on Flow Blue, and secondly for display in the museum collection. The project was started in 1968. Some of the items were very inexpensive and others carried a high price. Some dealers raised their price on an item because they knew that it was needed for the collection; others lowered their price for the same reason. We purchased cracked and chipped ware when that was all that was available in an elusive pattern. There is no way of learning from an individual piece of china whether it was part of a dinner set or not. Also, in some cases the maker may be obscure and the pattern odd or unique. Therefore the letter **"X"**, refers to an EXTRANEOUS pattern that cannot easily be fitted into lists A, B, C, D or E. The average cost of these odd pieces, ranging from late saucers to old plates was about $13.50.

HOW TO USE THE VALUE GUIDES
AND THE FLOW BLUE INDEX

PATTERN CATEGORIES ARE MARKED:

O – Oriental   A.N. – Art Nouveau

S – Scenic   B – Brush Stroke

F – Floral   M – Miscellaneous

BOOK REFERENCES ARE MARKED:

I – Flow Blue China an Aid to Identification

II – Flow Blue China II

III – Flow Blue China and Mulberry Ware

LIST REFERENCE:

A Early Victorian 1840-1860-1870

B Late Victorian Ware 1880–c. 1900

C Late Victorian Miscellaneous 1880–c. 1900

D Art Nouveau c. 1900

E Specialties

X Extraneous patterns

VALUE REFERENCE:

A+ High price   C   Average price

A   Average price   D+ High price

A– Lower than prices given   D   Average price

B+ High price   D– Lower than given

B   Average price   E   Average

B– Lower than price given   X   No value given

A

ABBEY (S), I . . . . B–

ACADIA (S), I, II . . . . B–

ACANTHA (F), I, II X

ACME (M), II X

ACORN (M), II C

ADAMS (M), II C

AGRA (S), I . . . . B–

ALASKA (AN), I . . . . .D

ALBANY, Grindley (F), I . . . . B

ALBANY, Johnson (AN), I . . . . .D

ALBERTA (F), II X

ALBION (M), II X

ALDINE (M), III . . . . B–

ALEXANDRA (M), II X

ALEXANDRIA (F), I X

ALMA, Adderly (F), II X

ALMA, Thomson (M), I . . . . A–

ALMA, Unknown (AN), II . . . . .D–

ALPHABET MUG (M) , III C

ALTHEA (F), III X

ALTON (AN), II . . . . .D–

AMBROSIA (F), I . . . . A–

AMERILLIA (F), I . . . . A–

AMOUR (O), I . . . . .A

AMOY (O), I . . . . A+

ANCIENT RUINS (S), I X

ANDORRA (AN), I . . . . .D

ANEMONE, B & B (F), I,II,III . . . . B–

ANEMONE, B & S (F), I X

ANEMONE, H & K (F), III X

ANEMQNE, V & B (F), III X

ANGELUS (The) (F), III X

ANGLESEA (AN), III . . . . .D

ANTIQUE BOTTLE (M), II . . . . .A–

APSLEY PLANT (F), II X

ARABESQUE, Kent (M), II C
ARABESQUE, Mayer (S), I . . . . .A
ARABIAN (M), I . . . . .A−
ARABIC (M), II X
ARCADIA, Plant (M), I X
ARCADIA, Wilkinson (F), I . . . . .B
ARGYLE, Ford (M), I . . . . .B−
ARGYLE, Grindley (M), I . . . . B+
ARGYLE, Hanley (F), I X
ARGYLE, Johnson (AN), I . . . . D+
ARGYLE, Myott (F), II . . . . .B−
ARGYLE, Wood (F), I, II . . . . .B−
ARGYLL (M), I . . . . .A−
ASHBURTON (F), I . . . . .B−
ASIA (O), II . . . . .A−
ASIATIC BIRDS (O), II X
ASIATIC PHEASANTS, Hughes (M), III X
ASIATIC PHEASANTS, Meir (M), I X
ASTER (F), II X
ASTER & GRAPESHOT (B), II . . . . A−
ASTORIA, Empire (AN), II .D−
ASTORIA, Johnson (F), I, II .B−
ASTORIA, N.W.P. (F), II . . . . .B−
ASTORIA, Pitcairn (AN), II .D−
ASTORIA, Upper H. (M), II .B−
ASTRAL (AN), II . . . . .D−
ATALANTA (S), II X
ATHENS, Adams (S), I, II . . . . .A−
ATHENS, Grimwades (AN), I .D−
ATHENS, Meigh (S), I . . . . .A−
ATHOL (F), I . . . . .B−
ATLAS (F), II C
AUBREY (AN), II . . . . .D−
AULD LANG SYNE (M), I X
AURORA (M), II . . . . .A−
AUROREA (F), I . . . . .A−

AVA (F), I X

AVON, Booths (S), I X

AVON, Keeling (F), II X

AYR (F), I . . . . B—

AZALEA (F), II C

B

BALMORAL, Burgess (M), II . . . . B—

BALMORAL, Mann (F), II . . . . A—

BALMORAL, Meakin (AN), I . . . . D—

BALTIC (AN), II . . . . D

BAMBOO, Alcock (M), II . . . . A—

BAMBOO, Dimmock (O), I . . . . A

BARONIA (AN), I . . . . D—

BASKET (O), II X

BATH (F), I . . . . B—

BAVARIA (F), II X

BEATRICE (F), I . . . . B—

BEAUFORT (AN), I . . . . D

BEAUTIES OF CHINA (O), I, II . . . . A

BEDFORT (M), I X

BEGONIA, Gibson (F), II C

BELFORT (F), II . . . . B—

BELL (AN), II . . . . D—

BELL BORDER WITH FLOWER & FERN (M), II . . . . A—

BELL FLOWER (M), I . . . . E

BELMONT, Ford (AN), III . . . . D—

BELMONT, Grindley (AN), II C

BELMONT, Meakin (F), II X

BELMONT, Weatherly (M), III . . . . B—

BENTICK (F), I . . . . B

BERKLEY (AN), II . . . . D—

BERKLY (M), I X

BERLIN GROUPS (F), II . . . . A—

BERLIN VASE (M), I . . . . A—

BERRY (M), III . . . .

BERWICK (F), I . . . . .B–

BERYL (AN), I . . . . .D–

BEVERLY (AN), II . . . . .D–

BIRDS AT FOUNTAIN (S), II X

BIRMAH (O), II . . . . .A–

BLACKBERRY (M), I . . . . .B

BLEEDING HEART (B), II . . . . .A–

BLENHEIM (AN), II . . . . .D–

BLOSSOM (F), I . . . . .B

BLUEBELL (M), I X

BLUEBELL WITH CHERRY BORDER (B), II . . . . .A–

BLUEBELL AND GRAPES (B), II . . . . .A–

BLUE DANUBE (AN), I . . . . .D

BLUE MEISSEN (M), I . . . . .B

BLUE ROSE (F), I . . . . .B

BOLINGBROKE, THE (F), II . . . . .B

BOMBAY (O), I X

BOMBAY JAPAN (O), II X

BONITA (F), III . . . . .B

BORDEAUX (F), II X

BOSPHORUS (S), II X

BOTANICAL (F), II . . . . .A

BOUQUET, Alcock (F), I . . . . .B

BOUQUET, Brownfield (M), II .X

BOUQUET, F. & W. (F), I X

BOUQUET, Nowotny (F), II X

BOUQUET, W & B (F) X

BRAMBLE (F), I X

BRAMPTON (AN), I . . . . .D–

BRAZIL (M), II . . . . .B–

BRENTFORD (AN), II . . . . .D–

BRIAR ROSE (AN), I C

BRIGHTON (F), I X

BRISTOL (M), III X

BROOKLYN, Johnson (AN), I .D

BROOKLYN, Maddock (F), I X

BROOKLYN, Myott (F), II . . . . B—

BROOKLYN, S & W (S), II . . . . B—

BROSELE (O), II X

BRUGGE (M), I X

BRUNSWICK (F), I . . . . .B

BRUNSWICK EVANGELINE (S), II . . . . .E

BRUSSELS (F), I, II . . . . B—

BRYONIA (M), II . . . . B—

BUCCLEUCH (M), I . . . . A—

BURLEIGH (AN), I . . . . .D

BURLINGTON (F), III . . . . B—

BURLINGTON, Cauldon (M), II . . . . .E

BURMESE, Emery (O), II X

BURMESE, W. (O), II X

BURNHAM (AN), II . . . . D—

BUTE, Ford (M), II . . . . D—

BYZANTINE (F), II . . . . B—

BYZANTIUM (O), II . . . . B+

C

CABUL (O), II . . . . A—

CAIRO (M), I X

CALCUTTA (O), I, II . . . . .A

CALENDAR PLATE I (M), III . . . . .E

CALENDAR PLATE II (M), III . . . . .E

CALIFORNIA (S), II . . . . A—

CAMBRIDGE, H & K (AN), II . . . . D—

CAMBRIDGE, Meakin (AN), I . . . . .D

CAMBRIDGE, N.W.P. (F), I . . . . B+

CAMELLIA (F), III X

CAMPION (F), I, III C

CANDIA (AN), I, II . . . . .D

CANNISTER (M), II C

CANTON, Ashworth (O), II . . . . B—

CANTON, Edwards (O), II . . . . .A

CANTON, Maddock (O), I . . . . A

CANTON GRUP (O), II .X

CANTON VINE (M), II . . . . A—

CAPRI (F), I X

CARLTON, Alcock (O), I . . . . A

CARLTON, Ford (M), III X

CASHMERE (O), I . . . . A+

CASTLE (S), III . . . . A—

CASTRO (M), I . . . . .B

CATHERINE (F), I . . . . B—

CATHERINE MERMET (F), I . . . . B—

CATHLYN (M), I, III X

CAVENDISH (M), I X

CECIL (F), I . . . . .B

CEICEL (F), I . . . . B—

CELESTE (O), I X

CELTIC, Grindley (AN), I . . . . .D

CELTIC, Unknown (AN), I . . . . D—

CEYLON (O), I . . . . .B

CHAIN OF STATES (M), I . . . . .B

CHAING (O), I X

CHANG (O), II . . . . .B

CHAPLET (M), II . . . . B—

CHAPLET (M), I X

CHAPOO (O), I . . . . A+

CHARLESTON (F), I X

CHASE, THE (S), II . . . . .E

CHATSWORTH, Ford (F), II . . . . B—

CHATSWORTH, Hancock (F), I X

CHATSWORTH, Jones (F), II X

CHATSWORTH, Keeling (F), I X

CHATSWORTH, Myott (F), II . . . . B—

CHEESE DISH (M), I C

CHEESE DISH II (M), II C

CHELSEA (S), III C

CHELTENHAM (F), II .X

CHEN-SI (O), I . . . . .A

CHERRY (B), II . . . . A−

CHINA ASTER, Minton (M), III X

CHINA ASTER (F), II . . . . B−

CHINA ASTER, S & K (F), II . . . . B

CHINESE, Dimmock (O), I . . . . .A

CHINESE, Meir (O), II. . . . . A−

CHINESE, Wedgwood (O), I. . . . . B

CHINESE ARABESQUE (O), II X

CHINESE BELLS (O), II . . . . A−

CHINESE BOUQUET (O), III X

CHINESE DRAGON (O), II C

CHINESE JAR (O), I . . . . A−

CHINESE KEY & BASKET (O), II X

CHINESE LADIES (O), III . . . . A−

CHINESE PLANT (M), II . . . . A−

CHINESE SPORTS (O), III . . . . A−

CHINESE TREE (O), II . . . . A−

CHINESS (O), I . . . . A−

CHING (O), II . . . . A−

CHISWICK (F), II X

CHRYSANTHEUM, Myott (F), I C

CHRYSANTHEUM, Pratt (O), II . . . . A−

CHUSAN, Clementson (O), I . . . . A+

CHUSAN, Fell (O), I . . . . .A

CHUSAN, Morley (O), II . . . . B

CHUSAN, Wedgwood (O), I . . . . B

CIRCASSIA (O), I . . . . A−

CIRIS (O), I .X

CLAREMONT (F), I . . . . B

CLAREMONT GROUPS (F), I . . . . A−

CLARENCE (F), I . . . . B+

CLARENDON (AN), II . . . . .D−

CLARIDGE (F), I X

CLARISSA (F), I X

CLAYTON (F), I . . . . B−

CLEMATIS, Barker (F), II .C
CLEMATIS, Johnson (F), II C
CLEOPATRA (S), II . . . . .A−
CLEVENDON (F), I . . . . .E
CLIFTON, Ford (F), II . . . . .B−
CLIFTON, Grindley (AN), I . . . . .D
CLIFTON, Meakin (F), I . . . . .B−
CLOVER, Grindley (M), I . . . . .B−
CLOVER, Wedgwood (F), II . . . . .A−
CLUNY (M), II . . . . .B−
CLYDE (F), I . . . . .B−
CLYTIE (S), II . . . . .E
COBOURG (F), I . . . . .A−
COBURG, Dimmock (F), I . . . . .A−
COBURG, Edwards (S), I . . . . .A
COCKATOO (M), II, III X
COLESBURG (F), II C
COLONIAL (M), I . . . . .B
COLONIAL, Laughlin (F), II X
COLUMBIA (S), I . . . . .A−
COLWYN (F), II X
CONSTANCE (M), III .X
CONVOLVOLUS (F), II . . . . .A−
CONWAY (M), I . . . . .B+
CORA (F), I X
CORAL (M), II X
CORAL JAPAN (O), II . . . . .A−
CORBEILLE (M), II X
COREA, Clementson (O) . . . . .A
COREA, Wedgwood (F), III . . . . .B−
COREAN (O), I . . . . .A+
CORELLA (S), I . . . . .A−
COREYHILL (O), III X
CORINTHIAN (M), II .X
CORINTHIAN FLUTE (M), I . . . . .A−
CORONET (F), II . . . . .B−

COTTAGE (S), III . . . . A—
COUNTESS (M), I . . . . B—
COUNTRY PASTURES (S), II X
COUNTRY SCENES (S), II . . . . .B
COWS (S), II . . . . .E
CRANSTON (F), III X
CRAWFORD RANGES (M), II . . . . .E
CRETE (F), I X
CROSSED BANDS (B), II . . . . A—
CRUMLIN (AN), I . . . . .D
CUBA (M), II X
CYPRUS, Davenport (O), II . . . . A—
CYPRUS, Ridgway B. (M), I X

D

DAGGER BORDER (O), II . . . . A—
DAHLIA (B), II . . . . A—
DAHLIA, Upper Hanley (F),.I X
DAINTY (AN), I . . . . .D
DAISY, B. & L. (F), I . . . . B—
DAISY, Soc.Cer. (B), II X
DAISY SEVEN PETALS (B), II . . . . A—
DALIAH (M), II . . . . A—
DAMASK ROSE (F), II . . . . A—
DANUBE (M), I X
DARDENELLES (S), II X
DAVENPORT (AN), II . . . . .D—
DEAKIN PEARL (M), I . . . . A—
DELAMERE (AN), I . . . . .D
DELAWARE (F), III X
DELFT (AN), II . . . . .D—
DELHI, B & T (O), II . . . . A—
DELHI CORN (O), II X
DELHI, Unknown (O), II X
DELMAR (M), II . . . . B—
DEL MONTE (F), I . . . . B—

```
DELPH (M), I . . . . . . . . . . . . . . . . . . .X
DENMARK, Furnival (M), I  . . . . . . . . . . . .X
DENMARK, Minton (M), I . . . . . . . . . . . . .X
DENTON (AN), II  . . . . . . . . . . . . . . . .D –
DERBY, Furnival (M), II . . . . . . . . . . . . .X
DERBY, Grindley (F), II . . . . . . . . . . . . . B
DEVON, Ford (AN), III  . . . . . . . . . . . . .D
DEVON, Meakin (F), I . . . . . . . . . . . . . . B
DIAMOND LEAF CROSS (B), II . . . . . . . . .A—
DIANA (M), II  . . . . . . . . . . . . . . . . .B—
DOG ROSE (F), I . . . . . . . . . . . . . . . . .X
DON (AN), I  . . . . . . . . . . . . . . . . . .D
DORA (F), I  . . . . . . . . . . . . . . . . . .X
DOREEN (F), II  . . . . . . . . . . . . . . . . .X
DORIS (M), II  . . . . . . . . . . . . . . . . . .C
DOROTHY, Corn (F), I  . . . . . . . . . . . . .X
DOROTHY, Johnson (M), II . . . . . . . . . . .B—
DOROTHY, Upper H. (M), II . . . . . . . . . .B—
D'ORSAY JAPAN (O), II . . . . . . . . . . . . .X
DOT FLOWER (B), II  . . . . . . . . . . . . . .X
DOUGLAS (AN), I . . . . . . . . . . . . . . . .D
DOVER, Ford (AN), II . . . . . . . . . . . . . .C
DOVER, Grindley (M), III . . . . . . . . . . . .B—
DRESDEN (M), II  . . . . . . . . . . . . . . . .B—
DRESDEN SPRIGS (F), I  . . . . . . . . . . . .B—
DRESDON (F), II  . . . . . . . . . . . . . . . .B—
DUCHESS, Dunn Bennett (AN), (F), I, II . . . . . . . . . . .X
DUCHESS, Grindley (F), I  . . . . . . . . . . .B—
DUDLEY, Ford (AN), I  . . . . . . . . . . . . .D—
DUDLEY, Myott (F), I . . . . . . . . . . . . . .B—
DUNBARTON (F), II . . . . . . . . . . . . . . .X
DUNDEE (F), I . . . . . . . . . . . . . . . . . .B—
DUNKELD (F), I . . . . . . . . . . . . . . . . .B—
```

E

```
EAGLE & SHIELD (M), II . . . . . . . . . . . . . . . . . .A
```

EASTER GREETINGS, (M), III . . . . E

EASTERN FLOWERS (F), II . . . . A−

EASTERN PLANTS (F), I X

EASTERN VINES (M), III X

EASTWOOD (F), I . . . . B−

EBOR (F), I X

ECLIPSE, Alcock (M), III X

ECLIPSE, Johnson (M), I . . . . B−

EDGAR (F), I . . . . B−

EGERTON (AN), I . . . . .D−

EGG BASKET (M), I X

EGLANTINE, K & G (F), II . . . . B−

EGLANTINE, Meigh (F), II . . . . A−

EGLINGTON TOURNAMENT (S), II . . . . B+

EL BRAU (F), I X

ELGAR (AN), II . . . . .D

ELIZABETH (F), II C

ELSA (M), I . . . . B−

ELSIE (F), II . . . . B−

ENGLAND (M), II X

ENGLISH ROSE (F), II C

ERIE (M), II . . . . B−

ETON (M), I . . . . B−

ETRUSCAN (M), II . . . . A−

EUPHRATES (O), I . . . . A−

EXCELSIOR, Fell (S), I . . . . .A

EXCELSIOR, Regout (M), I X

F

FAIRY VILLAS I (F), I X

FAIRY VILLAS II (O), I . . . . B+

FAIRY VILLAS III (O), I . . . . B+

FEATHER EDGE (M), I X

FERN (B), II . . . . A−

FERN AND BAR (B), II . . . . A−

FERN AND TULIP (B), II . . . . A−

FESTOON, Grindley (M), II C
FESTOON, Wilkerson (M), II X
FISHERMAN (O), II .A−
FISH PLATE (M), I . . . . .E
FISH PLATE II (S), II .E
FLAMINGO (M), I, III . . . . .E
FLENSBURG, III . . . . .A−
FLEUR-DE-LIS, Copeland (M) . . . . B−
FLEUR-DE-LIS, Meakin (M), I . . . . B−
FLORA, C & C (F), II .A−
FLORA, Davenport (F), III . . . . .A−
FLORA, Myotts (AN), I . . . . .D−
FLORA, Nimy-Belgium (F), I X
FLORA, Walker (M), II .A−
FLORA, Wilkinson (F), I .X
FLORAL (M), I . . . . B−
FLORAL GROUPS (F), II . . . . .A−
FLORENCE (M), I . . . . B−
FLORENTINE, Dean (F), I . . . . B−
FLORENTINE, Furnival (M), II . . . . B−
FLORENTINE PATTERN (M), III X
FLORIDA, Ford (F), I . . . . B−
FLORIDA, Grindley (F), I . . . . B+
FLORIDA, Johnson (AN), I . . . . D+
FLORIS (M), II . . . . B−
FLOWER BASKET (M), II X
FLOYDS AMHERST JAPAN (O), II X
FOLEY (F), I C
FONT (O), II . . . . B−
FORGET-ME-NOT (F), II X
FORMOSA, Jones (O), I . . . . .A−
FORMOSA, Mayer (O), I .A
FORMOSA, Ridgway (O), I . . . . A+
FORMOSA, Southwick (O), II . . . . .A−
FORTUNA (M), I, II . . . . B−
FRANCE (M), II . . . . .E

```
FRUIT BASKET (M), II . . . . . . . . . . . . . . . . . . A—
FRUITS AND FLOWERS (F), III . . . . . . . . . . . . .X
FULTON (AN), I . . . . . . . . . . . . . . . . . . . . . .D—
```

G

```
GAINSBOROUGH (M), I . . . . . . . . . . . . . . . . .B—
GAME BIRDS, Adams (S), II . . . . . . . . . . . . . . . .E
GAME BIRDS, Copeland (M), I . . . . . . . . . . . . . .E
GARLAND, B. & L. (F), III . . . . . . . . . . . . . . . .X
GARLAND, Corn (F), II . . . . . . . . . . . . . . . . .B—
GARLAND, Wood (F), I . . . . . . . . . . . . . . . . .B—
GAUDY BLUEBELL (B), III . . . . . . . . . . . . . . . .A
GEISHA, Ford (O), II . . . . . . . . . . . . . . . . . .X
GEISHA, Upper H. (O), I, II . . . . . . . . . . . . . . B+
GEM, Alcock (M), I . . . . . . . . . . . . . . . . . . .B—
GEM, Hammersley (M) . . . . . . . . . . . . . . . . . .A
GEM, Maddock (F), II . . . . . . . . . . . . . . . . . .B—
GEM, Meir (M), I . . . . . . . . . . . . . . . . . . . .B—
GENEVA, Doulton (S), I . . . . . . . . . . . . . . . . .B
GENEVA, N.W.P. (AN), I . . . . . . . . . . . . . . . . .D
GENEVESE (S), I . . . . . . . . . . . . . . . . . . . B+
GEORGIA (AN), I . . . . . . . . . . . . . . . . . . . .D
GERANEUM (F), III . . . . . . . . . . . . . . . . . . A—
GERANIUM (F), II . . . . . . . . . . . . . . . . . . . A—
GINGHAM FLOWER (B), III . . . . . . . . . . . . . . A—
GIRONDE (F), I . . . . . . . . . . . . . . . . . . . . .B—
GIRTON (AN), II . . . . . . . . . . . . . . . . . . . .D—
GLADIOLUS (F), II . . . . . . . . . . . . . . . . . . . .C
GLADYS (AN), I . . . . . . . . . . . . . . . . . . . . .D
GLEN (F), II . . . . . . . . . . . . . . . . . . . . . . .X
GLENWOOD (M), I . . . . . . . . . . . . . . . . . . .B—
GLOIRE de DIJON (F), I, II . . . . . . . . . . . . . . .C
GOTHA (S), I . . . . . . . . . . . . . . . . . . . . . . .A
GOTHIC, Furnival (S), I . . . . . . . . . . . . . . . . .A
GOTHIC, Meigh (M), II . . . . . . . . . . . . . . . . .X
GRACE (F), I . . . . . . . . . . . . . . . . . . . . . .B—
```

GRAND BOUQUET (M), III . . . . B–

GRAPES (B), II X

GRAPES AND LEAVES W/BLUE BAND (B), II . . . . A–

GRAPEVINE PUNCH BOWL (M), II C

GRASSHOPPER AND FLOWERS (O), II X

GRECIAN (M), II X

GRECIAN (S), I . . . . .B

GRECIAN SCROLL (S), I . . . . A–

GRECIAN STATUE (S), I .B

GRENADA (F), I . . . . B–

GRIFFIN (M), II . . . . .B

GROOP, THE (F), I . . . . .B

GROSVENOR (F), III . . . . A–

H

HAARLEM, B & L (AN), II . . . . D–

HAARLEM, V & B (F), II .X

HACKWOOD'S GARLAND (S), II . . . . A–

HADDON, Grindley (AN), I . . . . D+

HADDON, Libertas (AN), I . . . . .D

HAGUE (M), I . . . . B–

HAMILTON (F), I . . . . B–

HAMPTON (F), I X

HAMPTON SPRAY (F), II . . . . B–

HANGING BASKET (M), II X

HANNIBAL (M), I X

HARLINGTON (AN), II . . . . D–

HARROW (M), II C

HARVEST, Hancock (F), II X

HARVEST, Meakin (F), II . . . . B–

HARWOOD (F), II X

HASTINGS (F), I . . . . B–

HATFIELD (F), II X

HAT PIN HOLDER (M), I .C

HAWKSLEY (AN), II . . . . D--

HAWTHORNE (M), II . . . . .B

HEATH'S FLOWER (M), I . . . . A—
HERON, Meigh (M), II . . . . A—
HERON, Turner, II . . . . E
HEUMAN (M), II X
HILTON (AN), II . . . . .D—
HINDOOSTAN (O), II . . . . A—
HINDOSTAN (O), I . . . . A—
HINDUSTAN (O), I . . . . .A
HIZEN (O), III X
HOFBURG, THE (M), I . . . . B—
HOLLAND (M), I . . . . B+
HOLLAND, THE (M), I . . . . B—
HOMESTEAD, Meakin (S), I . . . . B—
HOMESTEAD, Unknown (S), II . . . . .B
HONC (O), I . . . . A—
HONG, P & G (O), I X
HONG, Unknown (O), II . . . . A—
HONG KONG, Meigh (O), I . . . . A+
HONG KONG, WRS (O), II . . . . A—
HONITON (AN), II . . . . .D—
HOT WATER DISH (M), I C
HUDSON, Meakin (F), I . . . . B—
HUDSON, R & M (M), I .E
HURON (F), I C
HYSON, Alcock (O), II .A
HYSON, Clementson (O), III . . . . .A

I

IDA (M), I . . . . .B
IDEAL (F), I . . . . B—
IDRIS (AN), I . . . . .D
ILFORD, Ford (M), I X
ILFORD, Keeling (F), II .X
IMPERIAL (M), II . . . . B—
IN THE BUNKER (S), III C
INDIA (O), II . . . . .B

INDIAN (O), I . . . . A+
INDIAN GARDEN (O), II X
INDIAN JAR (O), I . . . . .A
INDIAN PLANT (O), II . . . . .A—
INDIAN STONE (O), I . . . . .A
INDIAN TREE, Grimwades (M), III X
INDIAN TREE, Unknown (O), III . . . . .A
INDIANA (M), I X
IOWA, Wilkinson (F), I . . . . B
IPOMOEA (F), III .A—
IRENE (AN), II . . . . .D—
IRIS, Clementson (F), I . . . . B
IRIS, Corn (F), III . . . . B
IRIS, Myott (AN), II . . . . .D—
IRIS, Pearl Pottery (F), II C
IRIS, Wilkinson (AN), I . . . . .D
ISOLA BELLA (S), II . . . . B+
ISTHMIAN GAMES (S), II . . . . .A—
ITALIA (S), I X
ITALIAN URN (S), II X
IVANHOE (M), I . . . . B+
IVY, Myott (M), II . . . . B—
IVY, Unknown (M), I C

J

JANETTE (F), I . . . . B+
JAPAN, Bridgwood (O), I . . . . B—
JAPAN, Fell (O), I .A
JAPAN, Rathbone (M), III X
JAPAN, Unknown (O), II . . . . .A—
JAPAN PATTERN, Davenport (O), II X
JAPAN PATTERN, Meakin (O), II X
JAPANESE (O), I . . . . B
JAPANESE SCROLL (M), II . . . . .A—
JAQUEMINOT (F), I . . . . B
JARDINIERE (F), II .C

JARVA (O), I .X

JEDDO, Adams (S), I . . . . .B

JEDDO, Adams (O), I . . . . .A—

JEDDO, Brown W.M. (O), I . . . . .B

JENNY LIND (S), I . . . . .B

JEWEL, Johnson (AN), II . . . . .D

JEWEL, Maddock (M), II . . . . .B

JEWEL, Tams (M), II X

JEWELL (M), II X

JOSEPHINE (F), III . . . . B—

K

KAOLIN (O), II . . . . .A—

KEELE (M), I . . . . .B—

KELMSCOTT (AN), II . . . . .D—

KELVIN (F), I . . . . B+

KENDAL (F), II . . . . .B

KENSINGTON (AN), I . . . . .D—

KENT, Doulton (AN), II C

KENT, Grindley (M), II . . . . B—

KENTUCKY FRONTIER (S), III X

KENWOOD (F), II C

KENWORTH (M), I . . . . .B

KESWICK (F), I . . . . B—

KILLARNEY (F), I . . . . B—

KIN SHAN (O), I . . . . .A

KIRKEE (O), I . . . . .A

KNIGHT TEMPLAR (M), I . . . . B+

KNOX (AN), I . . . . .D

KREMLIN (O), II . . . . .A

KYBER, Meir (O), I . . . . .A

KYBER, Adams (O), I . . . . B+

L

LA BELLE (F), I . . . . B+

LA BELLE, LOVELY LADIES (M), I . . . . .B

LADAS (F), I . . . . B–

LADYBUG (F), II X

LA FRANCAISE (M), I . . . . B–

LAHORE, Corn (O), I . . . . .B

LAHORE, Phillips (O), I . . . . .A

LAKE (S), II . . . . A–

LAKEWOOD (AN), I . . . . .D

LANCASTER, Corn (F), I . . . . B–

LANCASTER, N.W.P. (F), I . . . . B–

LANDSCAPE (O), II . . . . .E

LARCH (F), II . . . . B–

LAS PALMAS CANARIA (S), II X

LEAF & SWAG (B), II . . . . .A–

LEAVES & BAR (B), II . . . . .A–

LEEN (O), II . . . . .A–

LEICESTER, B & L (AN), I . . . . .D

LEICESTER, Hancock (S), I . . . . .B

LEIPSIC (S), II . . . . A–

LE PAVOT (F), I . . . . B–

LICHFIELD, Ridgways (AN), I . . . . .D–

LICHFIELD, Wilkinson (AN), II . . . . .D–

LILAC (F), I X

LILY, Adams (F), III . . . . .D–

LILY, Adderly (F), II C

LILY, B & T (F), II . . . . .A–

LILY, Dimmock (F), II . . . . .A–

LILY, Ford (F), I C

LILY, Johnson (F), I . . . . .D

LILY, Meakin (F), II . . . . B–

LILY, Morley (F), I . . . . A–

LIMOGES (F), II C

LINCOLN (M), III X

LINCOLN'S HOUSE (S), II . . . . .E

LINDA (F), I . . . . B–

LINTIN (O), I . . . . .A

LOBELIA (F), I . . . . A–

LOIS (M), I . . . . B—
LONDON (S), II X
LONSDALE (M), I . . . . B+
LORCH (F), I . . . . B—
LORNE (AN), I . . . . .D
LORRAINE (F), I X
LOTUS, C & H (F), II C
LOTUS, Grindley (AN), I . . . . .D
LOTUS & LEAVES (B), II X
LOUISE, Grindley (F), I . . . . B—
LOUISE, Maddock (F), III C
LOUISE, N.W.P. (F), II . . . . B—
LOURVE (M), I . . . . B—
LOVELY LADY DRIVER (M), III . . . . .E
LOZERE (S), I . . . . A—
LUCANIA, Corn (AN), I . . . . .D—
LUCANIA, Clarke (F), II . . . . B—
LUCERNE, Dimmock (F), I . . . . B—
LUCERNE, N.W.P. (M), III X
LUGANO (F), I . . . . .B
LUNEVILLE (M), I .B
LUNEVILLE BLUE (M), I . . . . .B
LUNEVILLE ONION (M), I . . . . B—
LUSITANIA, Colley (AN), III . . . . .D—
LUSITANIA, Wood (AN), II . . . . .D—
LUSTRE BAND (B), II . . . . A—
LUZERNE (F), I . . . . B—
LYNDHURST (AN), I . . . . .D
LYNTON (F), II C

M

MABEL, II . . . . B—
MABELLE, II . . . . B—
MACOA (O), II . . . . A—
MADISON (M), I . . . . B—
MADRAS, Alcock (O), II . . . . A—

MADRAS, Doulton (O), I . . . . B+
MADRAS, N.W.P. (AN), I . . . . .D
MADRAS, Upper H. (M), II X
MALO (F), II . . . . A−
MALLOW (F), II C
MALTA (S), I X
MALTA, Grindley (M), II . . . . B−
MALTESE (O), I X
MALTESE CROSS BAND & STRIPE (B), II X
MALVERN (AN), I . . . . .D−
MANDARIN, Dimmock (O), II . . . . .A−
MANDARIN, Maddock (O), II . . . . .A−
MANDARIN, Pountney (O), I X
MANHATTAN (F), I . . . . B−
MANILLA, Podmore W. (O), I . . . . A+
MANILLA, Ridgway (O), III . . . . .A−
MANOR, The (S), III X
MAPLE LEAF (M), I X
MARCUS (S), I X
MARECHAL NEIL (F), I . . . . .B
MARGUERITE (F), I . . . . .B
MARIE (AN), I . . . . .D
MARIGOLD (F), II C
MARINE (S), II . . . . .E
MARLBOROUGH, Grindley (M), I . . . . .B
MARLBOROUGH, Wood (F), II C
MARQUIS, THE (M), I . . . . .B
MARQUIS, THE II, (M), III . . . . B−
MARTHA (F), I . . . . B−
MARTHA WASHINGTON (M), I . . . . B
MATLOCK (F), II X
MATTEAN (S), I . . . . B−
MAY (F), II C
McKINLEY (F), I . . . . B−
NcNETTE (S), I X
MEDALLION (O), III X

MEDIAEVAL (S), II . . . . .E
MEDWAY (F), II C
MEISSEN, Libertas (F), I . . . . B—
MEISSEN, F. Mehlen (F), I . . . . B—
MEISSEN, Minton (M), II . . . . .A—
MEISSEN, Ridgways (M), I X
MELBOURNE (F), I . . . . .B
MELROSE (F), I . . . . B—
MELTON (F), I C
MEMPHIS (O), III . . . . .E
MENTONE, Johnson (F), II . . . . B—
MENTONE, Meakin (F), I . . . . B—
MERION (F), I . . . . B—
MESSINA, Cauldon (F), I . . . . B—
MESSINA, Meakin (F), I . . . . B—
MIKADO, Corn (F), I . . . . B—
MIKADO, Furnival (O), II X
MILAN (M), I . . . . B—
MILFORD (AN), I . . . . .D—
MILLAIS (F), I X
MILTON (F), II . . . . B—
MINTON JAPAN (O), III . . . . .A
MINWOOD (M), II X
MIRA (F), I X
MOGUL (O), II X
MONARCH (M), I . . . . B—
MONGOLIA (M), I . . . . B—
MONTANA (F), I . . . . B—
MONTEREY (S), III X
MONTILLA (S), II . . . . .A—
MONTROSE (AN), II . . . . .D—
MOORISH PALACE (S), II . . . . .E
MOREA (S), II . . . . .A—
MORNING GLORY, Ashworth (F), II . . . . .A—
MORNING GLORY, Hughes (F), I . . . . B—
MORNING GLORY, Ridgway (F), I . . . . .A—

MORNING GLORY, Unknown (F), II . . . . .A—
MORRISAN, Doulton (M), I . . . . .B+
MORRISIAN, Doulton (S), II . . . . .B+
MOSELLE (S), III . . . . .A—
MOSS ROSE I (F), I . . . . .A—
MOSS ROSE II (F), I . . . . .A—
MOSS ROSE III (F), II . . . . .A—
MOSS ROSE, Ridgway (F), III . . . . .A—
MOUNTAIN STREAM (S) . . . . .E
MOWCOP (F), III X
MOYUNE (M), I . . . . .B
MURIEL (AN), I . . . . .D

N

NANCY, Grimwades (AN), I . . . . .D—
NANCY, Unknown (AN), I . . . . .D—
NANCY, Wedgwood (F), I C
NANKIN, Ashworth (M), I . . . . .B
NANKIN, Cauldon (O), II X
NANKIN, Davenport (F), I . . . . .A
NANKIN, Mellor (O), II . . . . .A—
NANKIN, Pratt (O), I . . . . .A
NANKIN, W. & B. (O), III . . . . .A—
NANKING (F), I . . . . .B
NATAL (AN), II . . . . .D—
NAVARRE (AN), I . . . . .D
NAVY (F), I, II . . . . .B
NELSON (F), III . . . . .B—
NEOPOLITAN (F), I . . . . .B—
NEWLIN (AN), II . . . . .D—
NIAGARA (F), II X
NING PO (O), I . . . . .A
NIOBE (F), I X
NON PAREIL, Burgess & Leigh (S), I . . . . .B+
NON PAREIL, Meakin (F), II . . . . .B—
NORBURY (F), I, II C

```
NORFOLK (S), II . . . . . . . . . . . . . . . . . . . .X
NORMANDY (M), I . . . . . . . . . . . . . . . . . . B+
NORTHERN SCENERY (S), II . . . . . . . . . . . . . . . B
NORTHUMBERLAND (M), II . . . . . . . . . . . . . . .X
NORWICH (F), I . . . . . . . . . . . . . . . . . . . B
```

O

```
OAKLAND (F), II . . . . . . . . . . . . . . . . . . .X
OCHIS (AN), III . . . . . . . . . . . . . . . . . .D–
OLD CASTLE (S), I . . . . . . . . . . . . . . . . . B
OLD CURIOSITY SHOP (S), II . . . . . . . . . . . . . B
OLYMPIA (F), I . . . . . . . . . . . . . . . . . . B–
ONION (M), II . . . . . . . . . . . . . . . . . . . B–
OPHIR (F), I . . . . . . . . . . . . . . . . . . . B
ORCHID (F), II . . . . . . . . . . . . . . . . . . B–
OREGON, Johnson (AN), I . . . . . . . . . . . . . .D
OREGON, Mayer (O), I . . . . . . . . . . . . . . . A+
ORIENTAL, Alcock (O), I . . . . . . . . . . . . . . .A
ORIENTAL, Dimmock (O), II . . . . . . . . . . . . .A–
ORIENTAL, Empire (O), I . . . . . . . . . . . . . . B
ORIENTAL, Kent (S), I . . . . . . . . . . . . . . .X
ORIENTAL, N.W.P. (O), I . . . . . . . . . . . . . . B
ORIENTAL, Regout (O), I . . . . . . . . . . . . . .X
ORIENTAL, Ridgways (O), I . . . . . . . . . . . . . B
ORIENTAL, Spode (O), II . . . . . . . . . . . . . . .A
ORIENTAL GARDEN (O), II . . . . . . . . . . . . . .X
ORMONDE (F), I . . . . . . . . . . . . . . . . . . B
OSBORNE, Ford (F), I . . . . . . . . . . . . . . . B–
OSBORNE, Grindley (F), I . . . . . . . . . . . . . B+
OSBORNE, J.R.B. (M), II . . . . . . . . . . . . . .X
OSBORNE, Rathbone (AN), I . . . . . . . . . . . . .D–
OSBORNE, Ridgways (F), I . . . . . . . . . . . . . B–
OSBORNE, Till (AN), II . . . . . . . . . . . . . .D–
OVANDO (F), I . . . . . . . . . . . . . . . . . . B
OXFORD, Adderly (AN), III . . . . . . . . . . . . .D–
OXFORD, Ford (AN), I . . . . . . . . . . . . . . .D
```

OXFORD, Johnson (AN), II . . . . .D
OYAMA (O), I . . . . .C.

P

PAGODA, P.B. & S (O), II . . . . B
PAGODA, Ridgway (O), I . . . . .A
PAGODA, Till (O), II . . . . B–
PAISLEY (M), I . . . . B–
PA JONG (O), I X
PALERMO (S), II . . . . A–
PANAMA CANAL (M), III . . . . .E
PANSIES, E.P.CO. (F), II . . . . B–
PANSIES, Sebring (F), II . . . . B–
PANSY, Johnson (F), II .C
PANSY, Unknown (F), I . . . . B–
PAR (M), II X
PARIS, Colley (AN), I . . . . .D–
PARIS, Johnson (F), II X
PARIS, N.W.P. (AN), I . . . . D+
PARISIAN (M), II . . . . .A
PARROT (M), II C
PARTHENON (S), II . . . . A–
PASSION FLOWER (F), II . . . . A–
PASTORAL (S), II . . . . B+
PEACH BLOSSOM (B), II . . . . A–
PEACH ROYAL (F), I . . . . .B
PEARL (F), II X
PEKIN, Davenport (O), II . . . . A–
PEKIN, Dimmock (O), I . . . . .A
PEKIN, Jones (O), I . . . . B–
PEKIN, Keeling (M), III . . . . A–
PEKIN, W & B (O), II . . . . A–
PEKIN, Wilkinson (O), I .B
PEKIN, Wood (O), II X
PEKING, Podmore Walker (O), I . . . . .A
PEKING, Unknown (O), II . . . . A–

PELEW (O), I . . . . A+
PENANG, Ford (M), III X
PENANG, Ridgway (O), I . . . . .A
PEONY, Meakin (F), I C
PEONY, Ridgways (F), II C
PERCY, Cifle (M), I . . . . .B
PERCY, Morley (S), III . . . . .A–
PERSIA (AN), II .D–
PERSIAN (AN), I .D+
PERSIAN BIRD (O), II . . . . .A–
PERSIAN FANS (M), II . . . . .B–
PERSIAN MEDALLION (M), II . . . . .B–
PERSIAN MOSS (M), I . . . . .B–
PERSIAN SCROLL (M), II . . . . .B–
PERSIAN SPRAY (M), III . . . . .B
PERTH (F), II C
PERUVIAN (S), II . . . . .A–
PERUVIAN HORSE HUNT (M), I X
PETUNIA, C & H (F), III C
PETUNIA, W & R (F), II . . . . .B–
PHEASANT (M), I .A–
PHOEBE (F), III .X
PICKWICK (M), I .B
PLATA (M), II X
PLEASURE GARDEN (O), II . . . . .A–
PLYMOUTH (F), I, II . . . . .B–
POMONA, Beardmore & Co. (M), I X
POMONA, B & W (M), II . . . . .B–
POMONA, Ridgways (F), III C
POPPEA (F), II .C
POPPIES (F), II .B–
POPPY, Adams (AN), II . . . . .D–
POPPY, Grindley (F), I . . . . .B
POPPY, Johnson (F), II C
POPPY, Meigh (F), III . . . . .A–
POPPY, N.W.P. (AN), I . . . . .D

POPPY, Till (F), III C
POPPY, Wedgwood (AN), I . . . . .D–
POPPY, Unknown (F), III .B–
PORTMAN (AN), I . . . . D
PORTSMOUTH (AN), I . . . . .D–
POSY WREATH, (B), II . . . . .A–
PRINCE (F), II C
PRINCESS, Beech (M) . . . . .B–
PRINCESS, Booth (F), I X
PRINCESS, Wood (F), II .C
PRINCETON (AN), I . . . . .D
PROGRESS (F), I . . . . .B–
PRUNUS (F), III . . . . .B

Q

QUAN TUNG (O), II . . . . .A–
QUEBEC (M), II . . . . .B–
QUEEN, Ford (F), III C
QUEEN, Rathbone (M), II . . . . .B–
QUEEN CHARLOTTE (F), I, II X
QUEENS BORDER (F), II . . . . .B–

R

RABBIT (S), II . . . . .E
RACINE (M), II . . . . .B–
RALEIGH (AN), I . . . . .D–
REBECCA (M), I X
RED BIRD (B), II . . . . .A–
REEDS AND FLOWERS (B), II . . . . .A–
REGAL (AN), II . . . . .D–
REGALIA (F), I C
REGENT, Johnson (AN), I . . . . .D–
REGENT, Meakin (AN), I . . . . .D
REGENT, Unknown (AN), I . . . . .D–
REGINA (M), II . . . . .B–
REGOUT'S FLOWER (AN), I, II . . . . .B

RENOWN (AN), II . . . . .D−

RHINE (S), I . . . . .A

RHINE GRAPE (M), II . . . . .B−

RHODA (F), III X

RHODA GARDENS (O), I . . . . .A

RHONE, Furnival (S), I . . . . .A

RHONE, W & B (S), I X

RHONE SCENERY (S), I, II . . . . .A−

RICHMOND, B & L (M), I .X

RICHMOND I, Ford (M), I .B−

RICHMOND II, Ford (M), III . . . . .B−

RICHMOND, Grindley (F), II . . . . .B−

RICHMOND, Johnson (F), I . . . . .B−

RICHMOND, Meakin (F), I .B−

RIDGWAY JAPAN (M), III .B

RINCEAUX (F), II X

RIO (O), II X

RIPON, Winkle (F), I C

RIPON, W & H (F), I . . . . .B

ROCK (O), I . . . . .A−

ROMA (F), I X

ROMANCE (S), II X

ROMEO (F), I . . . . .B−

ROOSEVELT (M), I . . . . .E

RORSTRAND ORIENTAL (O), III . . . . .A−

ROSALIE (F), I . . . . .B−

ROSE, B & L (F), II C

ROSE, Grindley (F), I . . . . .B

ROSE, Keeling (F), II . . . . .B

ROSE, Ridgways (F), II . . . . .B−

ROSE AND IVY, II . . . . .B

ROSE AND JESSAMINE (F), II C

ROSE SPRAYS (F), III . . . . .B−

ROSEBUD (M), II . . . . .B−

ROSEDALE (F), II . . . . .B−

ROSERIE (F), II X

ROSEVILLE (AN), I . . . . D–
ROSLIN (AN), II . . . . D–
ROWENA (F), II . . . . B–
ROXBURY (F), I . . . . .B
ROYAL (F), I C
ROYAL BLUE (M), I . . . . B–
ROYAL ROSE (M), II .X
ROYSTON (AN), I . . . . .D–
RUBUS (M), I, II X
RUINS (S), II . . . . A–
RUSKIN, Cauldon (F), I X
RUSKIN, Ford (S), II . . . . B–
RUSTIC (F), III . . . . B–

S

SABROAN (O), II . . . . A–
ST. LOUIS (F), II . . . . .B
ST. PETERSBURG (S), II . . . . .E
SARATOGA (M), I . . . . .E
SASKIA (F), II X
SAVOY (AN), I . . . . .D
SAXON (M), I X
SAXONY (M), II . . . . B–
SCENES OF QUEBEC (S), II . . . . .E
SCIAO (O), II X
SCINDE, Alcock (O), I . . . . A+
SCINDE, Walker (O), I . . . . .A
SEAWEED (B), II X
SEFTON (M), I, II . . . . B–
SEGAPORE (O), I . . . . A–
SENATOR (AN), II . . . . .D–
SEVILLE (AN), I . . . . .D
SEVRES (F), II . . . . B–
SHANGAE (O), I . . . . A–
SHANGHAI, Adams (O), I . . . . A–
SHANGHAI, Corn (O), I . . . . B–

SHANGHAI, Grindley (S), I . . . . B
SHANGHAI, Rathbone (M), II . . . . B–
SHANNON (M), II . . . . A–
SHAPOO (O), I . . . . A
SHARON (F), II C
SHELL, Challinor (M), I . . . . A
SHELL, Wedgwood (F), I X
SHELL AND FLOWER (M), III . . . . A–
SHIELD (S), I . . . . B+
SHUSAN (O), II . . . . A–
SIAM (O), II . . . . B
SIBYL (F), II X
SIMLA (O), I . . . . A–
SINGA (O), II . . . . A–
SINGAN (O), II, III . . . . A–
SIVA (O), I . . . . A–
SMYRNA (M), I . . . . A–
SNOW FLOWER (M), II C
SOBRAON (O), I . . . . A
SOLA (F), II C
SOMERSET (F), II X
SPANISH ROSE (F), II . . . . B
SPHINX (M), I . . . . A–
SPINACH (M), I . . . . B
SPINACH III (B), II . . . . B
SPINACH WITH CIRCLED FLOWER (B), II . . . . B–
SPLENDID (F), I X
SPRIGS (M), III . . . . A–
SPRINGFIELD (F), III . . . . B–
SPRINGTIME (M), III X
STAG ISLAND (S), II . . . . E
STANLEY (M), I . . . . B–
STAR WITH GOTHIC TRIM (B), III X
STELLA (M), I X
STERLING, Johnson (AN), I . . . . D–
STERLING, N.W.P. (F), I X

STERLING, U.S.A. (M), I . . . . B—
STICK SPATTER (B), II . . . . .A
STORK (S), III . . . . .E
STRATFORD, Grindley (M), I . . . . .B
STRATFORD, Ridgway (F), II X
STRAWBERRY (M), I . . . . .A
STRAWBERRY LUSTER (M), I . . . . .A
SOUVENIR, CHAUTAUQUA (S), III . . . . .E
SOUVENIR, OLD ORCHARD BEECH (S), III . . . . .E
SOUVENIR, PORT ARTHUR (S), III . . . . .E
SUMMERTIME (F), II . . . . B—
SUNFLOWER (F), II . . . . .B
SUNFLOWERS (O), III X
SUPERIOR, Regout (M), II . . . . B—
SUHRNGLEN (F), III . . . . .B
SUTHERLAND BORDER (M), I . . . . .B
SUTTON (F), I . . . . B—
SWALLOW (F), II . . . . B—
SWEETBRIER (F), II C
SWISS (S), II . . . . A—
SYBIL (F), III C
SYDNEY (F), I . . . . B—
SYLVAN (S), II . . . . .B
SYLVIA (O), III . . . . A—
SYRIA (S), II . . . . A—
SYRIAN (M), II C
SYTON (M), II . . . . B—

T

TAIWAN (O), I X
TANKARD (AN), II C
TASAN (M), II . . . . A—
TEMPLE, British Anchor (O), I . . . . B—
TEMPLE, W & B (O), II . . . . A—
TEMPLE, W & F (S), I, II . . . . A—
TEMPLE, THE (O), I . . . . .Λ+

123

THEBAN (S), II . . . . .E

THREE PETALS & LEAVES (B), II . . . . A—

TILE (M), I X

TIMOR (O), I, II . . . . A—

TINE (F), II . . . . .B

TINGHAI (O), III . . . . A—

TIVOLI, Furnival (S), I . . . . A—

TIVOLI, Meigh (S), III . . . . A—

TOGO, H & K (F), II . . . . B—

TOGO, F. Winkle (S), I . . . . B—

TOKIO, Johnson (AN), II . . . . .D—

TOKIO, Keeling (F), I . . . . B—

TOKIO, Mehlen (O), I X

TONQUIN, Adams (O), I . . . . .A

TONQUIN, Carr (O), II . . . . A—

TONQUIN, C & Y (O), II . . . . A—

TONQUIN, Heath (O), I . . . . A+

TONQUIN, Meir (O), I . . . . A—

TOOTHBRUSH HOLDER (M), II C

TORBAY (F), I X

TOURAINE (F), I . . . . B+

TOWER (S), II . . . . B—

TRELLIS (M), II C

TRENT, B & S (AN), II C

TRENT, Ford (M), I . . . . B—

TRENT, N.W.P. (AN), I . . . . .D

TRENT I, Wood (M), I . . . . B+

TRENT II, Wood (F), I . . . . .B

TRIESTE, THE (AN), II . . . . .D—

TRILBY (F), I . . . . B—

TRIPOD (O), I X

TROY (S), I . . . . A—

TRURO (AN), I . . . . .D—

TULIP (F), II X

TULIP AND SPRIG (B), II . . . . A—

TULIP LUSTRE (B), III . . . . A—

TULIPS (F), II C

TULIPS AND LEAVES (B), II . . . . .A—

TURIN (F), I, III X

TURKEY, Cauldon (S), III . . . . .E

TURKEY, Ridgways (S), II . . . . .E

TYCOON (O), II . . . . .B

TYG (O), III . . . . .A

TYNE (F), I, II X

TYROLEAN (S), I . . . . .A—

U

U.S.S. NEW YORK (S), II . . . . .E

V

VALENCIA (S), II . . . . .B—

VASE A LA CHINOISE (O), II C

VELARIAN (F), II . . . . .A—

VENETIAN SCENERY (S), II . . . . .B

VENICE, B & S (S), I C

VENICE, Johnson (F), I . . . . .B—

VENICE, P.B. & H. (M), II . . . . .A—

VENICE, Unknown (F), II . . . . .B—

VENTNOR (AN), I . . . . .D—

VENUS (M), II . . . . .B—

VERMONT (F), I . . . . .B—

VERNON (F), I C

VERONA, Ford (S), I . . . . .B

VERONA, Meakin (AN), I . . . . .D—

VERONA, N.W.P. (M), I . . . . .B

VERONA, Ridgways (M), I . . . . .B

VERONA, Wood (M), I . . . . .B

VERSAILLES (F), I . . . . .B—

VICTOR (F), II C

VICTORIA, Grindley (AN), I . . . . .D—

VICTORIA, Wood (F), I . . . . .B—

VIENNA (F), I X

```
VIGNETTE (S), I . . . . . . . . . . . . . . . . . . . . . . . . .B
VINCA AND BEADS (B), II . . . . . . . . . . . . . . . . .A—
VINCENNES (S), III . . . . . . . . . . . . . . . . . . . . .A—
VINE, Davenport (M), I . . . . . . . . . . . . . . . . . . .B
VINE, Wedgwood (M), II . . . . . . . . . . . . . . . . . .B+
VINE, Wedgwood & Co. (M), II . . . . . . . . . . . . .B—
VINRANKA (M), I . . . . . . . . . . . . . . . . . . . . . . .B
VINTAGE (O), II . . . . . . . . . . . . . . . . . . . . . . . .B
VIOLA (F), I . . . . . . . . . . . . . . . . . . . . . . . . . . .X
VIOLETS (F), II . . . . . . . . . . . . . . . . . . . . . . . .B—
VIOLETTE (F), II . . . . . . . . . . . . . . . . . . . . . . .B—
VIRGINIA, Maddock (M), I . . . . . . . . . . . . . . . . .B
VIRGINIA, Meakin (S), II . . . . . . . . . . . . . . . . . .B—
VISTA (S), I . . . . . . . . . . . . . . . . . . . . . . . . . . .X
VOLANTE (M), III . . . . . . . . . . . . . . . . . . . . . . .B—
```

W

```
WALBECK (AN), II . . . . . . . . . . . . . . . . . . . . . .D—
WALDORF (F), I . . . . . . . . . . . . . . . . . . . . . . . .B+
WALMER (S), I . . . . . . . . . . . . . . . . . . . . . . . . .X
WALTON (F), II . . . . . . . . . . . . . . . . . . . . . . . . .X
WARWICK, Johnson (F), II . . . . . . . . . . . . . . . . .B
WARWICK, Podmore (S), II . . . . . . . . . . . . . . . .A—
WARWICK, Warwick (F), I . . . . . . . . . . . . . . . . .X
WARWICK PANSY (F), II . . . . . . . . . . . . . . . . .B—
WASHINGTON (S), I . . . . . . . . . . . . . . . . . . . . .A—
WASHINGTON VASE (S), I . . . . . . . . . . . . . . . . .A
WATER LILY (F), III . . . . . . . . . . . . . . . . . . . . .A—
WATER NYMPH (F), II . . . . . . . . . . . . . . . . . . . .A
WATTEAU, Davenport (S), I . . . . . . . . . . . . . . . .B+
WATTEAU, Doulton (S), I . . . . . . . . . . . . . . . . . .B+
WATTEAU, Edge Malkin (AN), I . . . . . . . . . . . . .D
WATTEAU, Meigh (S), I . . . . . . . . . . . . . . . . . . .A—
WATTEAU, N.W.P. (S), I . . . . . . . . . . . . . . . . . .B
WAVERLY, Grindley (AN), II . . . . . . . . . . . . . . .D
WAVERLY, Maddock (F), I . . . . . . . . . . . . . . . . .X
```

WEIR (M), I X
WELBECK (AN), II . . . . .D—
WENTWORTH (M), III X
WESTBOURNE (M), II . . . . B—
WHAMPOA (O), I . . . . .A
WHAMPOA, Keeling (O), III . . . . .A—
WHEEL (B), II . . . . .A
WILD ROSE, Adams (F), II . . . . B—
WILD ROSE, Geo. Jones (S), I X
WILD STRAWBERRY (B) II . . . . .A—
WILLOW, D & D (O), I . . . . B
WILLOW, Doulton (O), II . . . . B+
WILLOW, Keeling (O), II X
WILLOW, Unknown (O), II X
WIND FLOWER (F), I X
WINDSOR (M), II . . . . .B—
WINDSOR ROYAL (O), I . . . . B
WINDSOR SCROLL (M), I . . . . .A—
WINDSOR WREATH (F), II . . . . .A—
WISTERIA (F), I X
WOODLAND (F), II . . . . .B—
WREATH (F), II . . . . .A—

Y

YEDDO (O), I . . . . B
YEDO (O), II . . . . .A—
YELLOW RIVER (O), II X
YORK, B. W. M., III X
YORK, Corn (F), II X
YORK, Meakin (M), II . . . . .B—

Z

ZUYDER (M), III X

**THE STUDIO
FOUNTAIN HOUSE EAST**

A BRIEF INTRODUCTION TO MULBERRY WARE

Most of the Mulberry Ware still extant was made during the early Victorian era (1835-1855) in Staffordshire, England. It is earthenware and was produced by many of the eminent potters who were producing Flow Blue China. The transfer patterns that the potteries owned were a costly investment and their application was not limited to one printed color. A stone ware dish might be printed in a sharp dark cobalt, a Flow Blue cobalt, a Flow Blue steel blue, black, green, lavender, pink, light blue, red, rose, grey, brown, or in a shade of mulberry. It appears from the examples available for study, that the blue transfers were the most popular for a long time and therefore a large proportion of the earthenware products was colored blue to answer public demand. Cobalt was expensive and the early Victorian potters experimented with other chemicals in efforts to manufacture other colored ware that would prove to be both popular and profitable.

The potteries were also constantly faced with the problem of trying to please the fickle taste of the gentry who then (as now) set the style pace for the middle and lower classes. Simeon Shaw states on pages 234 and 235 of his book "History of the Staffordshire Potteries" (1829), "Very recently several of the most eminent manufacturers have introduced a method of ornament in Table and Dessert Services, similar to Tea Services, by the Black Printers using red, brown and green colours, for beautiful designs of flowers and landscapes, on Pottery greatly improved in quality, and shapes formed with additional taste and elegance. This pottery has a rich and delicate appearance, and owing to the *Blue having become so common*, the other is now obtaining a decided preference in most genteel circles." (The italics are mine.)

As a result of their experiments the potters discovered that the use of certain chemicals produced a combination of red, brown, grey and purple. The new and odd colour was quickly adopted by the novelty seeking public. It is this mixed colour that is known as mulberry.

Manganese carbonate ($MnCO_3$) produces purple brown when added to a lead glaze in quantities from 5 per cent to 10 per cent. Combined with copper and cobalt it produces black. Manganese Dioxide (MnO_2) is used in the same way. By varying the amounts of manganese carbonate the colouring obtained in the finished products may vary from a light greyish warm brown to a very dark purple brown, the latter a favorite colour of the Victorians, "puce". Puce is derived from the Latin word "pulex" which means flea; the dictionary gives the colour description of puce as "purplish brown or brownish purple". Mulberry is defined (as a colour) in the Oxford Universal Dictionary as a dark purplish colour like that of mulberries. When applied to Mulberry Ware, the word encompasses both these colours and more. Sepia is the word used by some dealers who are describing puce. Sepia is actually a greyish brown which resembles the colour of the ink derived from a pigment obtained from the secretion of certain cuttlefish. When the word is used to describe the colour of a transfer pattern it is incorrect to use it as a synonym for plain brown. Both sepia and puce are included by most dealers in this country in the broad category of Mulberry Ware. In the trade a large spectrum of brownish colours ranging from greyish browns to a very dark purplish sepia through dark brownish reds to light reddish or warm browns, with a slightly purple cast, is considered mulberry. If you know the background of the word, then the multi-colours embraced under the term Mulberry Ware become understandable.

To the English, in Victorian times, mulberry meant the colour of the berries of the black mulberry trees that grew in their country. There are different types of these trees; the white (morus alba) bears nearly white fruit and its leaves are used for feeding silkworms. The American red mulberry (morus rubra) bears a dark purple fruit and the morus nigra, black mulberry, is found in England and bears very dark fruit. The black mulberry is a native of the middle part of Asia but was introduced into England a thousand years ago and has become naturalized. The Oxford Universal Dictionary, which is English, defines the colour mulberry as a "dark purple" like that of mulberries. If you will take one of the berries from the trees found in America and break it and rub the flesh across a piece of paper, you will be surprised to see the different shades of red and brown that evolve. Pieces of the flesh of the berry dry a warm shade of blackish brown. In other words the warmth of red is always present in these shades. They are never cold as they would be if blue was the sub-dominant colour. Since the English Mulberry is much darker than the American berry it can be surmised that the colours obtained from pressing the English mulberries would be much darker, but the lighter shades from both are like the gradations of the colour, which can range from warm brown to grey brown and on to purplish brown.

Maroon, when used on transfer china ware, is obtained by the use of chromium which at a low temperature produces brown, but at a high temperature produces red. Chromium oxide (Cr_2O_3) gives a variety of colours that include shades of maroon when added to lead glaze and in the presence of tin oxide. A light maroon is certainly similar to one of the colour shades encompassed in the word "mulberry".

So the word "mulberry" when applied to Early Victorian transfer ware is like the word "Flow Blue". Both encompass many variants as far as the colour itself is concerned. It is important to understand that not all mulberry patterns are flown. Some are clearly applied with great care in order to present a sharp design. Others are soft and have a hazy look, and many are very flown on face and underside. "Washington Vase" is one of the most famous and popular designs made in mulberry; it falls into the sepia sector of the classification as it is usually printed with a warm greyish light brown. Some of the transfers in "Washington Vase" are sharp, others are blurred. Some are more brown than others and some are darker than others. The variations are interesting and one can conjecture that colour control was difficult. Cobalt was always a reliable colouring agent and its control in the kiln was not difficult. Reds were much more difficult to produce as heat affected the chemicals and the desired shade of red could turn to black if the heat in the kiln was not reduced quickly enough.

Some of the patterns listed in this book date around 1835 and from what Simeon Shaw wrote in 1829 we can guess that mulberry colours were manufactured in answer to the public cry for something new. But the popularity of mulberry did not last, as can be deduced from the fact that very little was made after 1855. Twenty years or less seems a short time for production but the output must have been prolific because mulberry is not uncommon in shops or at shows.

The following list, which is probably not at all complete, includes patterns in a wide spectrum of colours from almost black to light brownish red, but all are mulberry variants. Two or three examples were photographed although they are brown, because mulberry examples could not be located. This is clearly stated in each description. They are included because Laidecker or Kamm or both, stated they had seen such examples in Mulberry Ware and listed them as such.

Many devoted and conservative collectors, especially in the Northeast, have been acquiring Mulberry ware for years. The prices have always been high as compared to those asked for Flow Blue China. But the situation has reversed itself and currently Mulberry Ware, which, remember, is predominantly Early Victorian stoneware, is selling at a third or more under the prices prevailing for Flow Blue of the era.

A COMPENDIUM

OF

MULBERRY WARE PATTERNS

MULBERRY WARE

A LIST OF PATTERNS LOCATED TO DATE

(NOTE THAT NOT ALL OF THESE ARE FLOWN)

Many patterns found in Mulberry were also used to decorate Flow Blue China and therefore we will not picture those that are so duplicated. If a design is listed in the author's books on Flow Blue, the reader is directed to said books by the following method. (NOTE: Most all patterns date c. 1850-55.)

Book I refers to FLOW BLUE CHINA, AN AID TO IDENTIFICATION

Book II refers to FLOW BLUE CHINA II

Book III refers to FLOW BLUE CHINA AND MULBERRY WARE

ABBEY

Made by W. Adams & Sons

(Mark 22) page 59, VOLUME I

ABBEY

Made by Livesley Powell & Company

This ten sided plate is not paneled on the rim. Its edges are detailed with a row of spear point which is repeated around the well. The rim is decorated with three oval cartouches which contain a picture of a towered building flanked by trees and an arched bridge in the foreground. Foliated scrolls are placed at the top of the rim between the cartouches and the space towards the well is filled with concentric lines which terminate in a beaded band. The central scene shows the ruins of a large Gothic church. There are tall trees at the left. In the foreground, on the bank of a stream, there are a child, a man who is standing and pointing, and two seated women. The example photographed is brown but this pattern was made in mulberry according to all authorities.

English, marked L. P. & Company, Mk. 2386, E.V., c. 1855.

ACROPOLIS

Maker Unknown

This plate is unevenly scalloped and the white edge is detailed by a row of small scrolls. Below these there is a white band filled with tiny flowers and C scrolls. This inner row is interupted by pairs of cornucopia-shaped floral scrolls at six points around the rim, which form an arch over a large acanthus type leaf set upon a floral and scroll base. Morning glories are placed on a stippled background between the large vertical leaves. The outer scroll edge is repeated in white around the well.

Two tall pillars are placed at the left of the central scene. Behind them are tall trees and the ruins of a temple. Other temples are placed on hills in the background. In the foreground there are four people in costume; one, a man, wears a cape and a big hat and holds an open scroll, another man dressed in turban and pantaloons holds a long stick, a woman kneels near a child amidst flowers and pieces of broken monuments.

English, probably E.V.

ALHAMBRA

Maker Unknown

The upper rim of this saucer is decorated with pairs of large flowers that alternate with a large peony and buds. The floral designs are linked by ivy vines and leaves. The lower aim is covered with net. The well is encircled by a band of large and small diamonds.

The castle shown in the center is constructed with a big square tower at the right. The building is Gothic and is not Arabic. The front section is double arched, one above the other. The doorway steps lead down to water. At extreme right there are tall elm trees and the bank in the foreground is strewn with flowers.

The example photographed is brown It is shown because this pattern was made in mulberry according to earlier writers.

Probably English, probably E.V.

ALLEGHANY

Made by Thomas Goodfellow

The rim of this twelve sided panelled plate is decorated with a row of stems and little leaves. Five cartouches, set within a background of concentric lines, contain a scene very similar to the central picture. The cartouches are separated by small bouquets of roses flanked by white quatrefoils. Both rim designs are contained within a chain design.

The well is circled by a band of ovoid beads.

The central scene depicts a grassy bank in the foreground on which three persons and a small dog are standing. A large Warwick type vase is placed at the left. There are marble walls and a small urn and the usual tall elm at the right. A castle-like building with a long straight facade and square towers overlooks a river at the center of the scene and there are Alpine peaks and clouds in the background.

English, marked as above, Mk. 1738, E.V., c. 1850.

AMERILLIA

Made by Podmore, Walker & Co.

Page 167, VOLUME I

ARCHERY

Maker Unknown

The saucer photographed bears a rim pattern of three bouquets separated by triangular foliated reserves filled with diamond and dot diapering. These are contained at the top by a row of printed scallops and beads, and an outer edging of trefoils and dots.

In the central scene two women are standing near a large target set upon three legs. One woman is holding her bow and aiming an arrow at another target in the right distance. A tournament tent with a pennant flying from its peak is behind the archers, and there is a castle in the distance. A tall tree rises at the right. There are overscaled flowers in the foreground.

There is no name on the back: the number 13 appears in an oblong frame. Kamm attributes this pattern to the Herculaneum Pottery and dates it to 1830.

Probably English, probably E.V.

ATHENS

Made by W. Adams & Sons

Page 114, VOLUME II

ATHENS

Made by Charles Meigh

Page 61, VOLUME I

AURORA

Made by F. Morley

Page 236, VOLUME II

AVON

Maker Unknown

The rim of this plate is panelled in U shaped sections, and is covered with a design of morning glories, leaves and wheat.

A bouquet of mixed large flowers in an urn is placed in the center of the well. Roses, peonies and leaves are placed about the outside of the urn and on its pedestal base. A small butterfly hovers at the upper right. (Note that this center design also appears on "Non Pareil" by Dixon.)

BALMORAL

Made by William Adam & Sons

The edge of this scalloped plate is outlined by a row of zigzag lines. The design, contained at the top edge by printed scallops composed of scrolls and plain bands, covers the entire surface of the plate. It consists of baroque scrolls entwined with garlands of small flowers like morning glories and forget-me-nots. The scrolls are placed three-quarters of the way around the rim. In the fourth section there is a large arrangement of dahlias, peonies, leaves and buds which spreads across the well.

English, marked W. A. & S., Mk. 23, E.V., c. 1855.

BASKET

Maker Unknown

Page 29 Volume II

BEAUTIES OF CHINA

Made by Mellor, Venables & Co.

Page 13, VOLUME II

BIRD AND FRUIT

Maker Unknown

This unevenly scalloped plate is edged in white enhanced by a dark row of diamond beading. Three oblong cartouches are placed around the rim, these contain a flat basket filled with berries, small flowers and leaves. The reserves are separated by large lacy scrolls that form a central scallop shell form. Both designs are placed over a stippled background which is sprinkled with small crosses.

The central scene pictures an exotic bird with long tail feathers who is perched in the center of an arrangement of fruit and flowers.

Probably English, probably E.V.

BOCHARA

Made by John Edwards

This twelve sided dark edged plate is panelled and the rim design is divided into five parts by a Gothic triangular shield that terminates in a fleur-de-lis at the top of the well. Five groups of peonies are placed in the spaces between the Gothic designs.

The central scene is oriental. At the right there are over-scaled flowers and leaves placed in an urn which is perched upon rock forms. At the left there is a tea house placed upon an elevation and over an overscaled flower. A tall feathery tree rises behind the roof of the tea house and small figures can be discerned on the balcony at its right. An arched bridge crosses the center of the design and links the two large designs. There are two figures on the bridge at right under the large leaves. In the foreground there are lines depicting water and a small plant that resembles wisteria.

English, marked J. E., Mk. 1449, E. V., c. 1850.

BRYONIA

Made by Paul Utschneider & Co.

Page 237, VOLUME II

CABUL

Made by Edward Challinor

Page 32, VOLUME II

CALCUTTA

Made by Edward Challinor

Page 58, VOLUME I

CALEDONIA

Made by William Adams

This plate is brownish purple. It is scalloped and the edge is detailed by a narrow band of pointed loops. There are four scenes on the rim showing two men on a rock who are hunting stags, which are fleeing below. Cartouches containing a scroll design and a single flower separate the scenic reserves. The well is detailed by a ring of triangles that terminate in a ball and tassel. A small cross between the tassels gives a spear point effect. The central scene shows a hunter in Scottish garb. He is standing on a mountain crag with his dog. The skull of a stag lies at his feet. Caledonia is a name for Scotland.

English, marked (imp.) Adams, Mk. 18, E.V., c. 1840.

CANOVIAN

Made by James & Ralph Clews

This unevenly scalloped plate is outlined in white. The rim is decorated with six oval reserves containing bouquets that are placed against a darker background. The reserves are separated by a pair of crossed plumes. Tiny flowers form a garland around the reserves and under the plumes. The well is wreathed by a row of flowers and a pendant spear point design.

The central scene is dominated by a tall column at right, flowers twine up its height. A statue of a sitting woman, which is placed on a large rectangular sculptured pedestal, is in the foreground and a kneeling girl and a standing boy, both in peasant costume, are near the pedestal.

A Tuscan mansion is in the background. At left there are a tall tree, some flowers and a rounded urn on a pedestal.

English, marked R. & J. Clews, E.V., c. 1825.

CASTLE SCENERY

Made by Jacob Furnival

The decoration on this plate is Moorish in effect. The rim contains six arched reserves set against a reticulated background. In each arch there is a picture of a domed castle at the right and a large thick tree at left and mountains in the background. A row of spear point encircles the well.

The central scene is framed by Moorish arches at the top. There is a tall elm at the right and an allée of elms at extreme right. A walled terrace occupies the foreground. Tall pandanus trees are at left behind a wall. A very tall urn is placed on the right wall. Three women in oriental dress are in the center foreground. In the background one can see castles, bushes and trees and what appears to be a waterfall.

English, marked J. F., like Mark 1643, E.V., c. 1850.

CATHEDRAL

Maker Unknown

The outer edge of this saucer is detailed with a row of tiny spear point and a circle of printed beads. The rim design features three scrolled reserves that contain a bird set against a stippled background. The upper part of the rim is covered with diamond diapering contained by double arch forms centered with large flowers. A row of spear point encircles the well.

A large domed Cathedral is seen in the left distance in the central scene. It is placed behind some buildings, tall bushy trees and a river.

In the right foreground there is a pedestal and large urn filled with over scaled flowers, and there are other large flowers and sprigs in the foreground.

Probably English, and probably E.V.

CHUSAN

Made by Podmore Hall

Page 20 (bottom), VOLUME I

COBURG

Made by E. Challinor & Co.

The rim of this octagonal platter is covered with narrow horizontal lines. Placed over these there is a curving tracery of light scrolls and leaves which intertwine to form oval reserves and open spaces containing pairs of flowers. The well is wreathed with small snail-like scrolls that terminate in a leaf and comma form.

The central scene is dominated by a large waterfront chalet at the right. It has two ornamental towers and Gothic carved bargeboards, that frame a six-paned bay window. A low wall on the left of the chalet which terminated in a coned tower, extends into the water. A bridge crosses the water in the center of the design. In the distance there are other buildings, tall trees and mountains. Tall elm trees rise from flowers strewn banks on either side of the foreground, and in the center a boat containing two people is reflected in the water.

English, marked E. C. & Co., like Mk. 836, E.V., c. 1855.

COLOGNE

Made by John Alcock

The edge of this twelve sided plate is embossed with a narrow ridge. The pattern on the rim extends over the ridge to the edge, and consists of five large foliated teardrop designs set against a background of worm trails set over concentric lines. The well is encircled on the bottom of the rim by a plain dark band. A pattern of three scrolls and leaves is placed over the band at ten points and the bottom of the scrolls enter the well.

A Gothic arched pavilion is at the right beside a tall elm tree in the central scene. Behind it there is a castle. At left there is another tall elm, in the center there is a river. Two men, one seated, are grouped with two standing women on the river bank in the foreground. There are mountain peaks in the distance.

An example of this pattern has been located marked J. & G. Alcock, Mk. 68, E.V., c. 1847.

COREA

Made by J. Clementson
Page 76, VOLUME II

COREAN

Made by Podmore, Walker & Co.

Page 22, VOLUME I

CYPRUS

Made by Davenport

Page 39, VOLUME II

DAMASCUS

Made by W. Adams & Sons

This is a pattern very much like "Palestine" by the same maker but the border scenes differ and so does the band that outlines the scenes and which meets under the flower sections of the rim in diamond angles.

The central scene differs on different sized plates and on this saucer a chariot drawn by a black horse and a white one dominates the scene. An exotic tent-like garden house is at the right, a river in the center, and domed mosques and towers are on the left background. This printing is done in a light tannish red. This is one of the very few late mulberry patterns, but it copied an earlier one.

English, marked as above, Mk. 22, L.V., c. 1890.

DELHI

Page 36, (top) VOLUME I (marked M. T. & Co., mark not found)

DORA

Made by E. Challinor & Co.

A border of Greek key design circles the outer edge of this plate. The rim, which is embossed with an arch design, is covered with scrolls which join six harp figures that contain two fleur-de-lis and six heart designs centered at the top with a small triangle. The Greek key band is repeated around the well.

The bucolic center picture contains a house with peaked roof at the right which is placed beneath tall elm trees. There are towered buildings at left behind a wall. Cows are placed in the center at left and there are rocks and part of a pond in the foreground. Alpine peaks and clouds complete the circular picture.

English, marked as above, Mk. 835A, Registered July 28, 1856, E.V., c. 1856.

DRESDON

Made by E. Challinor & Co.

The twelve sided bowl photographed is the bottom of a butter dish. The outer edge is detailed with a border of beads and large spear point. The dish is covered with a design of three bouquets composed of various flowers and leaves and sprigs which are attached at the right to a small baroque scroll filled with treillage. In the center of the well there is a spray of forget-me-nots.

English, marked as above, Mk. 836, E.V., c. 1855.

EON

Made by George Wooliscroft

This is the famous windmill pattern. The rim contains four reserves; two are pastoral scenes of men with farm animals and a cart. The other pair picture a windmill set in a landscape. These panels are separated by scroll forms that are composed of stylized branches and flowers. The well is encircled by a spear point design.

The central scene presents the windmill at left, small farm buildings are in the center distance. At right the usual tall elms appear, a fence defines a sloping bank, and at the end of the fence there are three persons.

English, marked as above, Mk. 4308, E.V., c. 1852.

FLORA

Made by Hulme & Booth

The plate photographed is twelve sided and the narrow rim is panelled and its edge is outlined in a dark band and small leaves. Three sprays of roses and daisies are printed on the rim. These are separated by three small sprigs. The center design is large and consists of a full blown rose, bud and leaves, combined with a lily and one large spade shaped lily leaf. Pink and green have been used to overpaint the transfer design.

English, marked as above, mark not located. John Hulme potted at Lanes End until 1830. Booth & Sons potted there from 1830 to 1835, so it is possible that Hulme & Booth were partners in 1840.

FLORA

Made by T. Walker

Page 248, VOLUME II

FOLIAGE

Made by Edward Walley

The plate photographed is twelve sided and panelled. The rim pattern consists of five foliated cartouches containing a picture of a castle, a square tower and trees. The well is encircled by a row of fleur-de-lis which form a spear point design. The central scene shows a large castle at left center. Trees and a grassy bank are placed in front of the buildings which are situated on a river. At right there are tall elm trees and in the foreground at left there is a parapet with a large urn placed on the top railing.

English, marked W. (imp.), Mk. 3990, E.V., c. 1850.

GENEVESE

Made by Ridgway

Page 64, VOLUME I

GENOA

Made by Davenport

This twelve sided plate has an edge trim of Gothic curved double lines. Six scroll cartouches contain a scene of a church-like building flanked by tall trees. These appear on the rim and are separated by keyhole designs containing little rose garlands. The bottoms of both designs enter the well and form a decorative wreath. The center scene is dominated by a wayside fountain and tall trees at the right. The fountain appears to be of stone or marble and contains a statue in the center. Water gushes from an opening beneath the feet of the statue into a wide basin. Two people on horseback are behind the basin at left and there are two seated figures at extreme left. Tall Alpine peaks complete the scene in the background. In the foreground there are flowers and what appears to be stones or rocks.

English, marked as above, Mk. 1181A, marked with an impressed and dated anchor, E.V., c. 1852.

GRECIAN SCENERY

Maker Unknown

This unevenly scalloped plate bears a rim design of six scenic reserves, three of which show a castle on the right and boats on a lake at left and three which reverse the castle location. Bouquets of flowers and leaves separate the scenes and a band of foliated scrolls against a dark beaded background outlines the outer edge of the plate. The well is encircled by a wreath of tiny bell flower designs. The central scene pictures a columned ruin at left. A large boat with oars and sails is on the river in the center and a tall exotic tree is behind the ruins. Three persons are in the foreground near a fallen column, two are standing and one is seated on the flower strewn ground.

English, marked "Stone China" E.V., c. 1850.

HEATH'S FLOWER

Made by T. Heath

Page 182 Volume I

HONG

Made by Thomas Walker

This plate is panelled and is fourteen sided. The edge is detailed on the upper rim by a Gothic design of eight banner shapes flanked by scrolls and a small oblong pattern of scrolls. The lower rim contains four scenes of a temple and these alternate with a peony and leaves. The well is surrounded by a band of lozenge patterned brocade.

The central picture contains a large garden house with upturned roof at the right. It is approached by a pebbled walkway and a flight of stairs. At the top of the stairs there is a small robed figure. A small slender tree composed of willow fronds, apples and flowers is in the center. At lower left there is a small building with upturned roof and in the foreground there are rounded rock forms. At a distance in the left background there is an island with a tower and a small boat is placed nearby.

English, marked as above, Mk. 3982, E.V., c. 1850.

HOP PICKERS

Maker Unknown

   This cup plate is printed in a brownish red. Its edge is gently scalloped and outlined by a row of tiny printed scallops. The rim design consists of a trailing vine with small flowers and sprigs. The design covers the well and shows a small boy kneeling on the grass. He is dropping a hop into a basket held by a girl. There is a house in the background, a tall tree at right, some bushes at left and overscaled flowers in the foreground.

   Probably English, probably E. V.

HYSON

Made by J. Clementson

Page 7, VOLUME III

ITALIAN URN

Maker Unknown

The cup plate photographed is scalloped. The edge is outlined in white. The rim pattern consists of four baroque cartouches that give a basket effect as they are filled with treillage topped by a garland. These are separated by pairs of wild roses. A row of deep red spear point encircles the well. A large urn at the right dominates the scene. It is filled with flowers and rests on a square base. At left in the foreground there is a low stone wall and a tall tree. In the distance there is a church with a very tall tower. A stream of water flows diagonally through the scene.

Probably English, probably E.V.

JEDDO

Made by W. Adams & Sons

Page 32, VOLUME I

KAN-SU

Made by Thomas Walker

This plate is fourteen sided and panelled. The rim design is composed of a large link chain. Six sections of the chain contain a cartouche scene of a European Gothic house, an arched bridge and trees; the other alternating six links, which are smaller, contain three realistic roses. The rim background is horizontally lined and small sprigs surround the outer edge. The well is encircled by a spear point design. The central scene depicts a lakeside pagoda at right. It has curved roofs and is capped with a pointed decoration. A pair of tall trees is at left. There is a sail boat near the pagoda. In the foreground at right there are bushes and other buildings and mountains are in the left background. Clouds are placed above the picture to complete the circle design.

English, marked as above, Mk. 3982, E.V., c. 1847.

KYBER

Made by John Meir & Son

Page 34, VOLUME I

LILY

Made by J. Furnival

The basin photographed is twelve sided and the deep sloping sides are panelled. The outer edge is wreathed by leaves and stems against a background of curved cloud-like lines. This wreath is repeated around the outside of the body of the vessel. There are three large groups of lilies, buds and leaves on the inside surface, and these are over-coloured with dark red, mustard yellow and green.

English, marked as above, like Mk. 1643, E.V.c. 1855

LINTIN

Made by Thos. Godwin

Page 36, VOLUME I

LORETTA

Made by Samuel Alcock & Co.

Five large cartouches are placed on the rim of this twelve sided plate. These contain a scene of a domed mosque flanked by tall trees. The cartouches are linked by a diamond shaped design composed of large serpentine Gothic scrolls placed on a dark ground of concentric lines. The well is encircled by a spear point design. The scene in the center is Venetian with the exception of the Alpine peaks in the background. At left there are domed buildings and a tower that resemble the buildings in St. Mark's Square in Venice. At right there are a very tall tree, a balustrade and some plantings. In the foreground on the tree-shaded bank of the river there are people standing near a path. A gondola approaches them.

English, marked as above, Mk. 76, E.V., c. 1850.

LOZERE

Made by Edward Challinor

Page 70, VOLUME I

MADRAS

Maker Unknown

Page 36, VOLUME I

MARMORA

Made by William Ridgway

The indented rim of this plate is printed with five different marine pictures which show Asian sailboats on rivers whose banks are lined with temples and columned ruins. These reserves are separated by a vertical trellis design with a fan shaped top, and are surmounted by wreaths of small flowers which, in turn, form a circle around the well.

The central scene shows a towered building at right, a tall elm at left and in the foreground there is a river with a fancy boat in which there are two fishermen. One has a net. Two persons are on the river bank in the center foreground.

This printing is in brown but the pattern was also made in mulberry according to many authorities.

English, marked W. R., Mk. 3301, E. V., c. 1850.

MEDINA

Made by Jacob Furnival & Co.

This saucer is fourteen sided and panelled. Concentric circular lines form the background of the rim design, and sprays of flowers are placed between six oval cartouches on the rim. Three of these reserves are small and contain a scene of a temple and a sail boat. The three larger ones contain a harbor scene. This printing which is done in sepia, features a well encircled by scalloped dotted lines and a small chain and square design.

The central scene is dominated by a two-tiered fountain in the right foreground. Four small figures are placed at its base and tall elm trees rise behind it. In the center there is a stream, and at left an open pavilion and trees. On the left bank, in the left background there are tall domed buildings, minarets, and mountain peaks. The tomb of Mohammed is of Medina and the building pictured is probably the great mosque of Medina.

English, marked J. F. & Co., Mk. 1643, E.V., c. 1850.

MISSOURI

Probably made by Broadhurst & Sons

The rim of this ten sided plate is covered with a paisley design set in wide oval cartouches confined by foliated scrolls. Small ovals form an edging around the top of the rim and fleur-de-lis contain the design at the bottom. The well is encircled by a narrow beaded band and a wreath of fleur-de-lis.

The central scene has nothing to do with the American state of Missouri, it is the usual romantic European scene. In the foreground there are Elizabethian costumed people on a railed terrace from which a stair rises to the right. Tall elm trees rise at both sides of the picture. In the left distance there are tall castle-like buildings. In the center there is a river and in the distance there are other buildings and mountains.

English, marked B. & S. Longton, E.V., dated 1855.

MOGUL SCENERY

Made by Thomas Mayer

The title does not appear on this scalloped cup plate shown, but the pattern conforms to the subject matter depicted and titled by T. Mayer. The border is composed of lacy swags that are draped under small flowers. The well is surrounded by sprigs. In the center a man riding a camel is in the foreground. At right there is a tall palm tree and behind the rider there is a domed building.

English, marked as above, with "Stoke", Mk. 2568, E.V., c. 1835.

MONTEZUMA

Made by J. Godwin

The rim of this sixteen sided saucer is decorated with four reserves containing a picture of a large two-storied manor house set between two large trees. A triangular design of grapes and leaves separates the scenic cartouches and trailing vines surround the outer edge. A ribbon of vertical lines is placed at the bottom of the rim and a saw tooth pattern encircles the well.

The central picture shows a tall palace at left which overlooks a river. Behind the castle there are very high Alpine peaks. In the foreground there are bushes at the left, a terrace and wide steps in the center, and at the right there is a large fountain. Its basin is supported by three cherubs and another cherub holds a cornucopia atop the basin.

Tall elms are placed to the right and behind the fountain.

English, marked as above with the word Longton, mark not located, but Godwin and Bullock potted in Longton from 1852 to 1856. E.V., c. 1850.

MOREA

Made by J. Goodwin

Page 97, VOLUME II

MOSS ROSE

Made by Jacob Furnival & Co.

Page 148, VOLUME II

NEVA

Made by Edward Challinor

This plate is fourteen sided and panelled. The rim design consists of scrolled arches containing a bell flower with a pendant. In the keyhole spaces formed between the arches, there are four-petaled flowers and leaves on top of a long square pendant. The flowers and the leaves in center resemble daffodils. They are flanked by small leafy stalks.

English, marked as above, Mk. 835A, E.V., c. 1850.

NING PO

Made by R. Hall & Co.

Page 39, VOLUME I

NON PAREIL

Made by Sunderland Pottery

This scalloped plate bears the same central picture as that which appears on the mulberry pattern "Avon" (maker unknown). But the borders are very different. The pattern on the rim of Non Pareil is composed of small grapes, tendrils and large leaves.

English, marked Dixon & Company, Mk. 3743, E.V., c. 1850.

ORIENTAL FLOWER

Made by Davenport

The edge of the twelve sided cup plate photographed is outlined by a row of snail-shell scrolls and enclosed by two narrow lines. The border design is composed of flowers, small pieces of fence and scrolls flanking a flower that give a butterfly effect. A large exotic flower and leaves are placed in the center of the well.

This plate is marked with only the makers name. No title is given to the pattern as is usual with cup plates. This name is used to present it.

English, marked as above. It also has an impressed anchor which is dated. Mk. 1181A, E.V., c. 1848.

"ORIENTAL SCENERY"

Made by T.J. & J. Mayer

This cup plate is white edged, scalloped and embossed with beaded scallops. A dark line printed with small loops and rosettes confines the rim pattern which consists of scrolls and flowers set against diamond diapering. In the center scene a domed temple on an island is at the left and a second domed temple is in the left background. A large boat with tall sails and high curved prow approaches the first building. It is oared, and there are men aboard holding spears, their round shields line the deck. The bow of the boat is shaped like a woman's face.

English, marked as above, Mk. 2570, E.V., c. 1850.

PALESTINE

Made by William Adams

This pattern appears on a scalloped plate and the edge is detailed by a narrow band of pointed loops. The rim is divided into four sections by scenic reserves showing domed buildings, minarets and a horseman. These alternate with pairs of large flowers and buds. A ribbon edging outlines both designs.

The central scene shows a tent-like garden house at right. Behind it there are palm trees. There are two people on a terrace in the foreground and domed buildings and mountains in the background.

This is very much like another pattern by the same maker, that is described in this book in the Mulberry section "Damascus".

English, marked (imp.) Adams, Mk. 24, E.V., c. 1835.

PANAMA

Made by Edward Challinor & Co.

The rim of this plate is panelled but the sides are not angled. A band of stylized leaves circles the outer edge. The rim is decorated with four oval foliated scenic cartouches containing a picture of a wide flight of stairs leading to a pair of towers with tall trees at the right. Four shields filled with a diamond design alternate with the cartouches. The rim background is filled with vertical lines and large foliated scrolls are placed over this. The well is encircled by a scroll pattern. The center scene is rustic and resembles a circular aperture in a forest.

In the foreground there are two children and a man. In the background there is a castle at left; there is a stream in the middle which is crossed by either a dam or an arched bridge. There are tall trees on either side of the river.

English, marked as above, Mk. 836, E.V., c. 1855.

PARK SCENERY

Probably made by G. Phillyn

The edge of this cup plate is detailed with a band of vertical bars. There are four rose buds, leaves and sprigs placed on the rim in a field of moire design. There is a wreath of sprigs and stylized flowers around the well.

In the center there is a cow and two sheep. At the left there is a paling enclosure and in the right distance there is a domed building.

There is no backstamp on the dish which is marked with a star and impressed asterisk. This name is used to catalogue the pattern.

English, marked "Longton", Mk.3012, E.V., c. 1842.

PELEW

Made by Edward Challinor & Co.

Page 45, VOLUME I

PERCY

Made by Morley

Page 18, VOLUME III

PERU

Made by Peter Holdcroft

The rim of the twelve sided and panelled plate shown is decorated with a narrow embossed outer edge. Three dark reserves containing Gothic scroll work are separated by sections of a trio of flowers, each in its own reserve, flanked by scrolled vertical bars, and placed on a small brick diapering. A row of scrolls contains the design at the outer edge, and a band of scrolls, fleur-de-lis and bell flowers form a wreath around the well.

The center scene is exotic. Domed towered buildings are at the left center. A tall elm is at right and in the center background there is a waterfall. Banana trees are placed on either side of the terrace. In the foreground a large urn is at the left on top of a square pedestal. Two small figures in oriental dress are standing, and two others are seated on the terrace steps.

English, marked Holdcroft & Co., see Goddon, page 328. Also marked imp. *"pearl"*, E.V., c. 1850.

PERUVIAN

Made by J. Wedgwood

Page 102, VOLUME II

RHODA GARDENS

Made by Heath

Page 46, VOLUME I

RHONE SCENERY

Made by T. J. & J. Mayer

Page 115, VOLUME II

RICHARD JORDON

Made by John Hall

This brownish red saucer is marked "The Residence of the late Richard Jordon, New Jersey". It is scalloped and the edge is outlined by a dark blue band. The rim is covered with flowers and scrolls and there is a fine spear point design of beading around the well. In the center there is a picture of Mr. Jordon, an early Quaker leader, standing in a fenced field. Behind him one sees his house at the right and a barn at the left and tall trees on either side of the fence.

English, marked J. H. & Co., mark not located, E.V., c. 1830.

ROSE

Made by Edward Challinor & Co.

The rim on this plate is embossed with horizontal arches and fleur-de-lis. The transfer in the center is the same as that used by Hulme and Booth on their "Flora" which is described in this Mulberry section, but the border on this plate is very different and so is the mold. The border on Rose consists of a dark outer edge and below that a row of scrolls. From these hang seven oval pendants. In the reserves formed between the pendants there are wild roses which alternate with a cultivated full blown rose and bud.

English, marked as above, with the word Tunstall, Mk. 835A, E.V., c. 1862.

ROSE

Made by Thomas Walker

The plate photographed is twelve sided and the rim is panelled and outlined by a dark outer band and a narrow inner line. The design consists of three wild roses, buds and leaves.

There is no title or backstamp on this plate. The maker's name is impressed. We will use the name Rose to present the pattern.

English, marked as above, marked T. Walker in a half circle, Mk. 3982A, E.V., c. 1850.

CHALLINOR   WALKER

ROSE & BELL

Made by Livesley Powell

    The entire surface of this ten sided plate is covered with a network on which there are superimposed small wild roses and sprigs of lily of the valley.

    The name appears on the back stamp in a cartouche formed by the same flowers.

    Marked L. P., Mk. 2386, E.V., c. 1855.

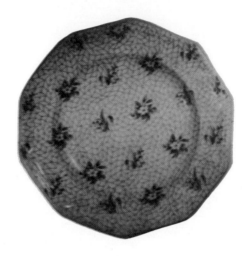

ROSELLE

Made by John Meir & Son

The distinctive rim design gives this pattern its name. Four baskets of roses are placed on a striated background and within cartouches formed by vines and trefoils. The latter twine to form a three lobed design between the flowers. Beading surrounds the well. This pattern is printed in purplish mulberry and does not flow.

The center scene shows a chalet type building at right. Across the river at the left there are tall graceful elm trees. In the left distance there are other buildings and mountains, and in the foreground there are flowering branches. The inside of the tea waste bowl is shown in order to show the basket of flowers in the bottom. (The chalet scene appears on the outside of the bowl.)

English, marked as above, Mk. 2636, E.V., c. 1848.

SCINDE

Made by Thomas Walker

Page 47, VOLUME I

SHAPOO

Made by Boote

Page 50, VOLUME I

SHELL AND FLOWERS

Made by Wedgwood & Co.

Page 58, VOLUME III

SIMLA

Made by Elsmore & Forster

Page 50, VOLUME I

SINGAN

Made by Goodfellow

Page 62, VOLUME III

SUSA

Made by Charles Meigh & Sons

The plate photographed is twelve sided and panelled. The rim design consists of five horizontal oval reserves that contain a picture of a Moorish temple, minarets and domed buildings. These are separated by a pendant and scroll design.

The well is encircled by a triple row of ovals centered with a dot which ends in points towards the center.

The central design depicts a river in the center. At left there are tall domed buildings and towers set against a mountainous background. At right there are mountains and a tall elm tree. Large banana trees are placed on each side of a terrace in the foreground and three people are placed on a rug at the center front.

English, marked C. M. & S., Mk. 2618, E.V., c. 1855.

SYDENHAN

Made by J. Clementson

A saucer is photographed in this pattern. The central scene differs in the various pieces of the dinner sets made. Most are Victorian statues of female figures, but on the cup a realistic mother and child are portrayed. The rim of the plates are decorated with three cartouches flanked by long foliated scrolls. Each reserve pictures a small statue and a handled urn. These alternate with three small oval cartouches which contain a picture of an urn on a pedestal base.

The rim of the saucer is divided into four such groups.

English, marked as above, also with a Phoenix mark, Mk. 910A, E.V., c. 1845.

SYLVIA

Made by J. Clementson

Page 11, VOLUME III

SYRIA

Made by Cochran

Page 106, VOLUME II

TAVOY

Made by Thomas Walker

This is the same pattern and border as Washington by the same maker. Washington is pictured in Book I, page 779.

TEMPLE

Made by Podmore, Walker & Co.

Page 53, VOLUME I

TEMPLE RUINS

Maker Unknown

The cup plate photographed is unevenly scalloped. Large foliated scrolls and various flowers are placed around the rim against a very dark purple reddish brov---The columns and arches of a large ancient temple are pictured in ruins in the cen. of the scene. Overscaled flowers are strewn across the foreground.

There is no back stamp on this plate. The name is used to catalogue t. pattern.

English, marked as above. Probably E.V.

TILLENBERG

Made by J. Clementson

The rim of this twelve sided panelled plate is decorated with three cartouches that contain a picture of a manor house. These alternate with three floral reserves. The well is encircled with a triple row of spear point design.

The central scene is the usual romanticized Swiss type with a large chalet and wall with watch tower that is situated beside a river. A tall elm grows from a grassy bank at the left. There are other buildings in the background. Clouds complete the circular design.

English, marked as above, 910A, Mk., E.V., c. 1845.

TIVOLI

Made by Charles Meigh & Sons

Page 20, VOLUME III

TONQUIN

Made by Heath

Page 55, VOLUME I

UDINA

Made by J. Clementson

Peonies are placed in baroque scrolled reserves on the rim of this twelve sided panelled plate. A flame design on a very dark ground fills the spaces between the cartouches at the top edge and small light flowers are used for the same purpose at the bottom. A wreath of scrolled flowers and leaves circles the well. Snowy Alpine peaks form the background for the central scene which contains a castle with slender tall rounded towers. This is placed at the left of the design. At the right there is a steep bank from which tall elms grow. At the foot of the bank there are four persons. A river divides the scene and a bridge crosses the water in the center. Small trees are placed on the flat bank in the left foreground.

English, marked as above. Also marked with a Phoenix bird design, Mk. 910A, E.V., c.1850.

188

VENETIAN SCENE

Made by Davenport

The edge of this scalloped toddy plate is decorated with small loops and a row of dark spear point. The rim is covered with floral bouquets and foliated triangular designs filled with quatrefoils and small scenic reserves containing a picture of a large statue of a seated figure holding a spear on an oblong pedestal. Exotic boats with sails are in the foreground of the central scene. In the background there are city buildings and a tower which are at waters edge as in Venice.

There is no name on the back stamp. This name is used to present the pattern. English, marked as above, also with an anchor, Mk. 81, E.V., c. 1840.

VENTURE

Made by Ralph Hammersley

This ten sided plate is printed in a brownish mulberry with a bluish purple edging. It is not flown. The rim is covered with a Gothic design of scrolls placed against a linear background. Six reserves contain a picture of a castle tower and a very large dark urn in the right foreground. These are separated by a design that resembles a basket filled with flowers. The well is encircled by a row of small scrolls and slanted tassels. The scene in the center has the usual tall elm at the left, a castle and mountain in the background, a river with one boat in the center. In the foreground there is a sharp bank at the right that slants toward the water. A covered urn atop a pedestal placed on a wall is at the right center, and there are three people, a man and two women with parasols, on the bank in the foreground.
Marked R. H., Mk. 1912, E.V., c. 1855.

VINCENNES

Made by Samuel Alcock

Page 21, VOLUME III

WALMER

Made by Elijah Hodgkinson

Page 78, VOLUME I

WASHINGTON VASE

Made by Podmore, Walker & Co.

Page 76, VOLUME I

WHAMPOA

Made by Dilwyn Swansea

Page 75, VOLUME II

WILD STRAWBERRY

Page 228, VOLUME II

WREATH

Made by Thomas Furnival & Co.

The plate pictured is twelve sided, the edge is outlined with a spear point design and the panelled rim is covered with a wreath of leaves, lilies and forget-me-nots.

A large full blown rose and its leaves is placed in the center. It is paired with several dahlias and buds on one stem at the left and is flanked by forget-me-nots.

English, marked T. F. & Co., and imp. real iron stone. Mk. 1645, E.V., c. 1845.

PATTERNS
LOCATED TOO LATE
TO PLACE IN CATEGORY

MULBERRY WARE

CAMBRIAN

Made by George Phillips

The word *Cambrian* means Welsh, (pertaining to Wales). This scalloped cup plate is white edged, and the rim is covered with a multi-flora pattern set against a background of small flowers. The rim design is contained at the top by a narrow scalloped band of tiny triangles.

The central scene depicts a farm. A double-storied cottage flanked by tall trees is at the right. Its upper story is approached by a steep flight of steps. In the left center a man is seated on a boulder and is conversing with a standing woman. There are flowers in the foreground and mountains and other buildings in the left background.

English, marked as above, Mk. 3010, E.V., c. 1842.

"LAWRENCE"

The central scene on this pattern resembles "Tillenberg". There is a large chalet at right, tall elm trees and a stone wall at left, mountain peaks in the background. In the foreground there are three people, two are seated on the grass and one stands. The usual river or stream courses through the center of the scene, and there is a small boat near the chalet ramparts.

The border is very different than that of Tillenberg. Small leaves and grapes on their vines twine over a background of horizontal lines in which oval reserves containing a picture of a large manor, lake, urn and wall at left and two standing persons in the foreground, alternate with a cross design composed of three foliated fan-like scrolls at top and bottom. This well is encircled by a small gothic design of arches and lines that give a spearpoint effect.

English (probably) marked S, Mk. not located. Probably E.V., c. 1850.

MOREA

Made by J. Goodwin

Page 97, VOLUME II

FLOW BLUE

INDIAN FESTOON
Maker Unknown
English, Registry date 1843 E.V., c. 1843

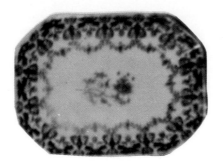

TILLENBERG

Page 187   VOLUME III

PATTERN CORRECTION TO BOOK II

page 270 **"TASAN".** *This should read "Fasan" which means pheasant in German. Marked V&B. Made by Villeroy and Boch in Germany. E.V., c. 1856.*

We show a picture of a deep dish in the pattern.

INDEX
FLOW BLUE PATTERNS

O – Oriental   F – Floral   M – Miscellaneous

S – Scenic   AN – Art Nouveau   B – Brush-Stroke Painted

* – Described or Named in Book I & II

	Page
*ACANTHA (F)	63
ALDINE (M)	48
ALTHEA (F)	24
ALPHABET MUG (M)	48
*ANEMONE, Minton (F)	61
ANEMONE, H & K (F)	24
ANEMONE, V & B (F)	24
ANGELUS, The (F)	25
ANGLESEA (AN)	40
ARABIA (O)	4
ASIATIC PHEASANTS, Hughes (M)	48
*ASTER AND GRAPE SHOT (BS)	64
*AURORA (M)	65
*BALTIC (AN)	64
BELMONT, Ford (AN)	40
BELMONT, Wetherby (M)	49
BERRY (M)	49
BONITA (F)	25
BRISTOL (M)	49
*BROOKLYN (F)	63
BURLINGTON (F)	25
CALENDAR PLATE I (M)	50
CALENDAR PLATE II (M)	50
CAMELLIA (F)	26
*CAMPION (F)	63
CARLTON, Ford (M)	51
CARNATION (F)	26
CASTLE (S)	14
CATHLYN (M)	51
*CHANG (O)	62
CHELSEA (S)	14
CHINA ASTER, Minton (M)	51
CHINESE BOUQUET (O)	4
CHINESE SPORTS (O)	5
*CHUSAN, Clementson (O)	61
*CHUSAN, R H & Co. (O)	63
*COCKATOO (M)	65
COLUMBIAN STAR (S)	15
CONSTANCE (M)	52
COREA (F)	27
COREY HILL (O)	5
COTTAGE (S)	15
CRANSTON (F)	27
CRAWFORD RANGES (M)	65

	Page
DELEWARE (F)	27
*DELPH (M)	61
*DERBY (F)	63
DEVON (AN)	41
DOVER (M)	52
*DUDLEY, Ford (AN)	61
EASTER GREETINGS (M)	52
EASTERN VINES (M)	53
ECLIPSE (M)	53
FLENSBURG (S)	16
FLORA (F)	28
FLORENTINE (F)	28
FLORENTINE PATTERN (M)	53
FRUIT AND FLOWERS (F)	28
GARLAND (F)	29
GAUDY BLUE BELL (BS)	44
GERANIUM (F)	29
GINGHAM FLOWER (BS)	44
GRAND BOUQUET (M)	54
GROSVENOR (F)	29
HIZEN (O)	5
HYSON (O)	6
INDIAN FESTOON (O)	194
INDIAN TREE, Grimwaldes (M)	54
INDIAN TREE, Unknown (O)	6
IN THE BUNKER (S)	16
IPOMOEA (F)	30
IRIS, Corn (F)	30
JAPAN, Rathbone (M)	54
*JARDINIERE (F)	63
JOSEPHINE (F)	30
LILY, Adams (F)	31
LINCOLN (M)	55
LOUISE (F)	31
LOVELY DRIVER (M)	55
LUEERNE, NYP (M)	55
LUSITANIA, Colley (AN)	41
*LUSTRE BAND (BS)	64

INDEX
FLOW BLUE PATTERNS

	Page
MANILA (O)	6
MANOR, The (S)	17
MARQUIS II (M)	56
MEDALLION (O)	7
MEMPHIS (O)	7
MINTON JAPAN (O)	8
MONTEREY (S)	17
MOSELLE (S)	18
MOSS ROSE, Ridgway (F)	31
MOWCOP (F)	32
NANKIN, W & B (O)	8
NAPIER (O)	9
NELSON (F)	32
OCHIS (AN)	42
OXFORD, Adderly (AN)	42
PANAMA CANAL (M)	56
*PANSY (F)	61
*PEACH BLOSSOM (BS)	65
PEKIN, Keeling (M)	57
PENANG, Ford (M)	57
PERCY (S)	18
PERSIAN SPRAY (M)	57
PETUNIA (F)	32
PHOEBE (F)	33
POMONA, Ridgway (F)	33
POPPY, Meigh (F)	33
POPPY, Till (F)	34
POPPY, Unknown (F)	34
PRUNUS (F)	34
QUEEN, Ford (F)	35
RHODA (F)	35
RICHMOND, Ford (M)	58
RIDGWAY JAPAN (M)	58
*RINCEAUX (F)	63
ROÖRSTRAND'S ORIENTAL (O)	10
ROSE SPRAYS (F)	35
RUSTIC (F)	36

	Page
SHELL AND FLOWER (M)	58
SICILIAN (O)	10
*SINGAN (O)	62
SOUVENIR, Chautauqua (S)	14
SOUVENIR, Maine (S)	19
SOUVENIR, Port Arthur (S)	19
SPRIGS (M)	59
SPRINGFIELD (F)	36
SPRINGTIME (M)	59
STAR (BS)	45
*STICK SPATTER (BS)	65
STORK (S)	20
SUHRNGLEN (F)	36
SUNFLOWERS (O)	11
SYBIL (F)	37
SYLVIA (O)	11
*SYRIA (M)	63
*SYRIAN (M)	65
TASAN (O)	194
TILLENBERG (S)	194
TINOLI (S)	20
*TOKIO (AN)	64
*TOWER (S)	63
*TURIN (F)	61
TULIP LUSTRE WITH CIRCLE (BS)	45
TURKEY, Cauldon (S)	21
TYG (O)	12
*TYROLEAN (S)	61
*VENETIAN SCENERY (S)	63
VINCENNES (S)	21
VOLANTE (M)	59
WAMPOA, Keeling (O)	12
WATER LILY (F)	37
WENTWORTH (M)	60
*WILLOW (O)	62
*YELLOW RIVER (O)	62
YORK, BWM (M)	60
*ZUYDER (M)	60

INDEX
MULBERRY WARE

	Page		Page
ABBEY	.137	HONG	.160
ABBEY	.137	HOP PICKERS	.161
ACROPOLIS	.138	HYSON	.161
ALHAMBRA	.139		
ALLEGHANY	.140	ITALIAN URN	.162
AMERILLIA	.140		
ARCHERY	.141	JEDDO	.162
ATHENS	.141		
ATHENS	.141	KAN-SU	.163
AURORA	.142	KYBER	.163
AVON	.142		
		LAWRENCE	.193
BALMORAL	.143	LILY	.164
BASKET	.143	LORETTA	.165
BEAUTIES OF CHINA	.143	LOZERE	.165
BIRD AND FRUIT	.144		
BOCHARA	.145	MADRAS	.166
BRYONIA	.145	MARMORA	.166
		MEDINA	.167
CABUL	.145	MISSOURI	.168
CALCUTTA	.146	MOGUL SCENERY	.169
CALCUTTA	.146	MONTEZUMA	.170
CALEDONIA	.146	MOSS ROSE	.170
CAMBRION	.192		
CANOVIAN	.147	NEVA	.171
CASTLE SCENERY	.148	NING PO	.171
CATHEDRAL	.149	NON PAREIL	.172
CHUSAN	.149		
COBURG	.150	ORIENTAL FLOWER	.173
COLOGNE	.151	"ORIENTAL SCENERY"	.174
COREA	.151		
COREAN	.152	PALESTINE	.175
CYPRUS	.152	PANAMA	.176
		PELEW	.176
DAMASCUS	.152	PERCY	.177
DELHI	.153	PERU	.177
DORA	.153	PERUVIAN	.177
DRESDON	.154		
		RHODA GARDENS	.178
EON	.155	RHONE SCENERY	.178
		RICHARD JORDON	.178
FLORA	.156	ROSE	.179
FLORA	.156	ROSE	.179
FOLIAGE	.157	ROSE AND BELL	.180
		ROSELLE	.181
GENEVESE	.157	RURAL SCENE	.182
GENOA	.158		
GRECIAN SCENERY	.159	SCINDE	.182
		SHAPOO	.182
HEATH'S FLOWER	.159	SHELL AND FLOWERS	.183

INDEX
MULBERRY WARE

	Page		Page
SIMLA	.182	UDINA	.188
SINGAN	.183		
SUSA	.183	VENETIAN SCENE	.189
SYDENHAN	.184	VENTURE	.190
SYLVIA	.184	VINCENNES	.190
SYRIA	.184		
		WALMER	.190
TAVOY	.185	WASHINGTON VASE	.191
TEMPLE	.185	WHAMPOA	.191
TEMPLE RUINS	.186	WILD STRAWBERRY	.191
TILLENBERG	.187	WREATH	.191
TIVOLI	.187		
TONQUIN	.187		

BOB KELLOGG

COVER PHOTOGRAPHS